TINKLE
DOUBLE

S0-BDR-092

THE GREATEST SHOW ON EARTH

Illustrations : V.B. Halbe

This story by Sigrun O. Srivastava won the Second Prize in the Tinkle Original Story Competition.

IN THE VILLAGE OF KRISHNAPUR LIVED A BOY NAMED TUTU. TUTU HAD MANY FRIENDS, BUT HIS BEST FRIENDS WERE BOO, THE OLD BUFFALO ON HIS FATHER'S FARM...

... AND HIS CLASSMATE, LASSI. ONE MORNING ―

LASSI, LASSI, LISTEN! OH WAKE UP, LASSI!

AAAH...

WHY, TUTU, WHAT HAS HAPPENED?

IT'S BOO, OUR BOO...

FATHER HAS GIVEN HIM ONLY ONE MONTH'S TIME TO STAY ON AT THE FARM. AFTER THAT, HE SAYS THAT I WILL HAVE TO ABANDON BOO IN THE FOREST.

I KNOW BOO IS OLD AND CANNOT WORK ANYMORE, BUT TO LEAVE HIM IN THE FOREST...! HE'LL BE LOST AND FRIENDLESS THERE.

TUTU, WE'LL NOT LET THAT HAPPEN. COME, LET'S THINK OF SOMETHING THAT WILL HELP SAVE BOO.

DO YOU THINK WE COULD TEACH HIM TO... TO ...

TO WHAT?

SO TUTU TOLD HIM.

NO, IT'S IMPOSSIBLE.

THAT AFTERNOON, THE TWO BOYS, MOUNTED ON BOO'S BACK, RODE DOWN TO THE RIVER BANK.

AND THERE...

NOW, LISTEN TO ME, BOO. WE ARE GOING TO TEACH YOU HOW TO DANCE.

MONKEYS, HORSES AND DOGS LEARN TO DANCE, THEN WHY NOT YOU?

COME ON, LASSI GIVE HIM THE BEAT. AND YOU BOO, WATCH ME.

COME ON BOO, LOOK AT MY FEET.

THRUM THRUM DHA!!

TAP TAP TAP TAP

DID YOU GET THAT, BOO?

BOO STARED GRAVELY AT TUTU. THEN —

AAAH!

OH, COME ON NOW! PAY ATTENTION, BOO. LET'S TRY AGAIN.

COME ON, TRY.

YOU CAN DO IT. I'M SURE YOU CAN.

BUT BOO JUST LOWERED HIS HEAD AND BEGAN TO CROP THE GRASS.

BOO, PLEASE LOOK AT ME. I'LL LIFT YOUR LEGS FOR YOU...

...THIS WAY, THAT WAY; THIS WAY, THAT WAY. NOW AGAIN!

SO LASSI STARTED TO BEAT THE DRUM AGAIN AND TUTU DANCED, BUT BOO DID NOT MOVE AN INCH!

TUTU, IT'S NO USE. I GIVE UP.

TUTU TURNED TO LASSI, TEARS GLISTENED IN HIS EYES.

OH LASSI, NO! WE HAVE TO TEACH HIM. HE HAS TO LEARN IT. THAT'S THE ONLY CHANCE WE'VE GOT.

THE FRIENDS TAUGHT BOO THE WHOLE AFTERNOON AND ALL THROUGH THE NEXT DAY AND THE WHOLE WEEK.

BUT BOO DID NOT LIFT HIS FEET.

TUTU, I GIVE UP. IT'S HOPELESS. THE FELLOW IS TOO STUPID TO LEARN ANYTHING.

LET'S GO HOME!

AND THE NEXT MOMENT—

LASSI, LASSI LOOK.

EING!

6

7

SO TEARING FOUR PAGES OUT OF THEIR OLD COPY BOOKS, LASSI BROUGHT OUT HIS RED AND BLUE INK PENS AND SET TO WORK.

THAT'S IT!

THE GREATEST SHOW ON EARTH! BOO THE WONDER BUFFALO SHOWS HIS WONDERFUL TRICKS! IT IS UNBELIEVABLE, BUT TRUE! FIRST SHOW ON SUNDAY AT 4 O'CLOCK UNDER THE THREE BANYAN TREES! ENTRANCE 20 PAISA! ALL ARE WELCOME! DONATIONS ARE WELCOME TOO!

I WISH I COULD ADD 'ART AND MUSIC DIRECTOR: LASSI KATTA SINGH', BUT THERE IS NO SPACE LEFT.

THE TWO FRIENDS PASTED THE FIRST POSTER BY THE SCHOOL DOOR (WHEN THE TEACHER WAS NOT AROUND) THE SECOND ON THE POST-BOX; THE THIRD IN KUNTIL MANDAL'S RICE SHOP AND THE FOURTH AT THE PAANWALLAH'S SHOP.

AND THAT SUNDAY...

HOW WONDERFUL BOO LOOKED AS THE BOYS MARCHED HIM PROUDLY DOWN TO THE THREE BANYAN TREES!

AND WHAT A CROWD HAD GATHERED! ALMOST EVERYBODY IN KRISHNAPUR WAS THERE.

HERE THEY COME! HURRAH! WHAT CAN THE WONDER BUFFALO DO?

PERHAPS HE CAN LAY A GOLD EGG!

HA, HA, HA! HO, HO, HO!

TUTU IGNORED THE SHOUTS OF LAUGHTER. THEN ...

SILENCE PLEASE! THE PERFORMANCE WILL NOW BEGIN.

BOO, BOO, DO YOUR BEST. DANCE, DANCE!

BUT BOO STOOD MOTIONLESS AND GAZED AT THE CROWD.

THEN SLOWLY, HE RAISED HIS HOOF AND ___

THE PEOPLE OF KRISHNAPUR HELD THEIR BREATH. THEY COULDN'T BELIEVE THEIR EYES!

THEN EVERYONE BURST INTO APPLAUSE! THE PAANWALLAH, THE POSTMAN, KUNTIL MANDAL FROM THE RICE-SHOP AND EVEN THE SCHOOL-TEACHER, CHEERED.

THEN TUTU CAME FORWARD.

ATTENTION! BOO WILL NOW BALANCE A BALL ON THE TIP OF HIS NOSE.

THE CROWD GASPED.

IMPOSSIBLE! NO BUFFALO CAN DO THAT.

BOO CAN!

NO, HE CANNOT!

EVERYONE TURNED TO SEE WHO HAD SPOKEN. IT WAS GURBACHAN SINGH, THE RICHEST FARMER IN THE VILLAGE.

NO BUFFALO HAS DONE IT AND NO BUFFALO EVER WILL. I CAN BET ON IT.

THERE WAS PIN-DROP SILENCE. THEN TUTU CLEARED HIS THROAT.

I ACCEPT THE BET.

GOOD!

AND THEY SHOOK HANDS ON IT.

10

TUTU'S HEART WAS IN HIS MOUTH AS HE WENT TO BOO.

I COUNT ON YOU TO DO IT. DON'T DROP THE BALL. FOR YOUR SAKE AND MINE, DON'T DROP IT.

BOO RAISED HIS HEAD.

START, BOO!

THE CROWD CLAPPED AND WHISTLED...

GOOD SHOW!

WE WANT MORE!

...WHILE GURBACHAN SHOOK HIS HEAD OVER AND OVER AGAIN IN DISBELIEF.

THEN HE QUIETLY PRESSED A NOTE INTO TUTU'S HAND.

BUY BOO SOME OILCAKES FOR HIS DINNER TONIGHT.

THEN TUTU GOT UP ON A BUCKET.

FRIENDS, AS YOU HAVE SEEN, BOO IS VERY CLEVER, BUT HE IS VERY OLD AND USELESS FOR WORK.

BUT HE IS MY FRIEND. I COULD NOT BEAR THE THOUGHT OF LEAVING HIM TO DIE IN THE FOREST.

WE NEED MONEY TO BUY FODDER FOR BOO SO HE CAN CONTINUE TO LIVE WITH US. COULD YOU PLEASE HELP US?

THE PEOPLE OF KRISHNAPUR BEGAN TO SHUFFLE THEIR FEET UNCOMFORTABLY. THEN A VOICE SPOKE. IT WAS FARMER GURBACHAN SINGH.

I ALSO THINK TUTU AND BOO DESERVE TO STAY TOGETHER.

THEREFORE, I'LL DONATE FODDER FOR BOO FOR THE REST OF HIS LIFE.

TUTU, THAT WAS A GOOD SHOW; INDEED IT WAS THE GREATEST SHOW ON EARTH.

THANK YOU, OH, THANK YOU SO MUCH!

BOO, LASSI... COME ON, LET'S DANCE!

LA, LA, LA, LA, LA, LA.

THRUM-BOOM THRUM-BOOM DHRUM-BOOM DHRUM-BOOM

JINGLE JINGLE JINGLE JINGLE

12

THE MONEYLENDER MEETS HIS MATCH

Illustrations Ram Waeerkar

Based on a story sent by Arup Jyoti, Nagaland

ONE AFTERNOON, IN A FOREST, A WOOD CUTTER WAS CHOPPING WOOD WHEN SUDDENLY, HE SAW A WILD BUFFALO CHARGING TOWARDS HIM.

AT ONCE, HE SHINNED UP A TREE.

THUD

THE BUFFALO RAMMED THE TREE AGAIN AND AGAIN...

HELP! HELP!

AFTER SOME TIME THE BUFFALO GREW TIRED...

FFF... HFFF...

...AND FELL ASLEEP.

SAVED!

NOW I'LL QUIETLY CLIMB DOWN AND...

14

WHEN THE MAN HAD CLIMBED UP —

NOW LISTEN — FOR A MONTH NOW, I HAVE BEEN THE KEEPER OF THIS BUFFALO.

MY JOB IS MERELY TO SIT ON THIS TREE AND MIND IT. WHEN I TAKE IT BACK TO THE PALACE IN THE EVENING, THE KING GIVES ME A THOUSAND GOLD COINS.

A THOUSAND GOLD COINS? FOR ONLY A DAY'S WORK?

YES — THAT'S HOW PRECIOUS THIS BUFFALO IS!

HAVING DONE THIS JOB FOR SO LONG, I HAVE BECOME A RICH MAN.

NOW I FEEL I SHOULD LET SOMEBODY ELSE MAKE SOME MONEY TOO.

HOW THOUGHTFUL AND KIND YOU ARE! I WILL GLADLY TAKE UP THE JOB!

A WISE DECISION!

THE BRUTE IS STILL ASLEEP. GOOD!

AS QUIETLY AS HE COULD THE WOODCUTTER CLIMBED DOWN THE TREE.

I MUST SIT ALL DAY ON THIS TREE, YOU SAID?

SSSH.... SSH ...YES, YES, OR YOU WON'T GET YOUR GOLD COINS.

SO ALL AFTERNOON, THE MONEY LENDER SAT ON THE TREE.

OOOH! HOW STIFF AND SORE MY LIMBS HAVE BECOME.

FINALLY, IN THE EVENING, HE CLIMBED DOWN.

GET UP, YOU! I WANT MY GOLD COINS.

GRRAH...!

OW!

AAAH! HE'LL GORE ME TO DEATH.

HELP!

IT WAS A LONG TIME BEFORE THE BUFFALO LEFT...

...AND THE TERRIFIED MAN COULD CLIMB DOWN AGAIN.

I... I NEVER WANT TO SEE A BUFFALO AGAIN!

You can't Fool Chachaji
Illustrations: Ashok Dongre

This story by Margaret Bhatty won the Consolation Prize in the Tinkle Original Story Competition.

IT WAS APRIL FOOL'S DAY. ASHA, DHIREN AND THEIR BELOVED CHACHAJI SAT ROUND THE TABLE.

OH THE JOKES WE PLAYED ON APRIL FOOL'S DAY, WHEN I WAS YOUNG! THEY WERE FULL OF WIT AND IMAGINATION.

WHAT'S THE MATTER? WHY ARE YOU STARING AT ME?

THERE IS A SMUDGE ON YOUR CHIN, CHACHAJI.

HA! HA! THAT IS A VERY STALE ONE, SON. YOU WILL HAVE TO BE SMARTER TO FOOL YOUR OLD CHACHAJI.

JUST THEN THE CHILDREN'S MOTHER CAME INTO THE ROOM.

THERE IS A SMUDGE ON YOUR CHIN, CHACHAJI.

THERE IS?

OOPS! IT MUST HAVE GOT THERE WHILE I WAS POLISHING MY SHOES.

HA! HA! WE TOLD YOU SO CHACHAJI.

AH, WELL I MUST BE OFF TO THE COURT.

17

I HAVE AN IMPORTANT CASE.

GROAN! HOW CAN ANYONE GET SO FAT OVERNIGHT!

APRIL FOOL!

APRIL FOOL CHACHAJI!

WHAT DO YOU MEAN?

WE SHIFTED THE POSITION OF YOUR BUTTONS BY THREE INCHES!

OH, YOU NAUGHTY CHILDREN!

THAT WAS A MEAN THING TO DO.

FORTUNATELY, I HAVE ANOTHER COAT.

THAT EVENING THE CHILDREN CAME HOME FROM SCHOOL FULL OF GLEE.

OH, CHACHAJI, THE JOKES WE PLAYED!

YOU SHOULD HAVE SEEN OUR TEACHER'S FACE WHEN SHE SAW THE UGLY INKBLOT ON HER REGISTER!

AND THEN POOF! I JUST LIFTED IT OFF HER BOOK. IT WAS A FAKE!

SHE WAS A GOOD SPORT, THOUGH!

WE'VE BROUGHT YOU SOME SWEETS CHACHAJI. HAVE ONE.

HMM, HOW NICE OF YOU.

BUT JUST IN TIME CHACHAJI REMEMBERED.

OH NO! OH NO! YOU CAN'T FOOL ME. THOSE TOFFEES ARE PROBABLY SOAP.

NO, HONESTLY, CHACHAJI. HAVE ONE.

NO! NO!

ANYWAY, I WILL LEAVE YOURS HERE ON THE TABLE. WE'RE GOING OUT.

A LITTLE LATER THE CHILDREN CAME RUNNING HOME.

CHACHAJI CHACHAJI, THE COURT HOUSE IS ON FIRE!

ARREY BHAI! THAT'S AN OLD JOKE. THINK OF SOMETHING BETTER.

TRULY CHACHAJI! TELEPHONE THE FIRE BRIGADE!

HA HA. YOU CANNOT FOOL ME THIS TIME.

19

21

22

THE ADVENTURES OF SUPPANDI-5

Illustrations: Ram Waeerkar   Based on a story sent by K. Bhagatchandra Singh, Goa

* WATER DRUNK AFTER EATING AMLA, TASTES SWEET

24

WHEN THEY REACHED THE MAN'S HOUSE —

I HOPE YOU'VE BROUGHT THE OIL. THERE'S NOT A DROP IN THE HOUSE.

YES, HERE IT IS.

WAIT HERE. I'LL PAY YOU SOMETHING FOR YOUR TROUBLE.

HUSBAND! IS THIS A TRICK? THIS IS NOT OIL, IT IS JUST PLAIN WATER!

OH! WHAT AM I GOING TO DO?

YOU! BOY! WHAT HAVE YOU DONE WITH THE OIL?

SIR, I HAD A DRINK OF WATER ON THE WAY. IT WAS SO VERY SWEET....

...SO VERY SWEET! I EMPTIED THE OIL AND BROUGHT WATER FOR YOU INSTEAD! AREN'T YOU HAPPY?

GRRRH....GET OUT OF MY SIGHT BEFORE I BREAK YOUR NECK!

FOOLS! NO APPRECIATION OF THE GOOD THINGS OF LIFE!

Kalia
THE CROW

Script
DEV NADKARNI

Illustrations
ASHOK DONGRE

HA, HA, THAT FIXES OUR MEAL FOR TODAY.

YES!

OH NO!

MUST DO SOMETHING!

SUDDENLY —

HELP! HELP! I'M STUCK.

HELP!

LOOKS LIKE IT'S OUR LUCKY DAY, DOOB DOOB. FIND OUT WHO'S CALLING FOR HELP, WILL YOU?

IT'S COMING FROM THAT PIT... I'LL GO AND SEE.

KA... KALIA.

HELP ME GET OUT, DOOB DOOB! MY FOOT IS STUCK.

GOOD NEWS, CHAMATAKA!

GUESS WHO'S STUCK IN THAT PIT?

SHONAR? SUNDAR? SUNDARI?

27

THE BASHFUL SON-IN-LAW

Script:
Gayatri Madan Dutt

Illustrations:
Ram Waeerkar

ONCE, A MAN KNOWN FOR HIS EXTREME SHYNESS, SET OUT FOR HIS MOTHER-IN-LAW'S HOUSE. HE TOOK A BARBER ALONG FOR COMPANY.

THEY WERE GIVEN A CORDIAL WELCOME.

WHAT A LOVELY SURPRISE! COME, YOU ARE JUST IN TIME FOR LUNCH.

UM! DELICIOUS RICE AND PICKLE!

PLEASE BEGIN. I'LL SIT BY TO SERVE YOU.

THE BARBER AT ONCE FELL UPON HIS FOOD WITH GUSTO...

...BUT THE SON-IN-LAW DID NOT.

WHAT'S WRONG?

29

WHY AREN'T YOU EATING SON-IN-LAW?

EAT? WITH YOU WATCHING?

?

HE MUST BE ILL!

I MUST SPEAK TO THE OTHER WOMEN ABOUT THIS.

SHE HURRIEDLY WENT AWAY...

...AND THE MOMENT HER BACK WAS TURNED—

AHA!

30

THE NEXT MINUTE—

SON-IN-LAW...

ULP!

... THE OTHERS FEEL THAT YOU MAY HAVE A TUMMY-UPSET. IS THAT WHAT'S WRONG?

OH! WHAT IS IT, MY CHILD?

HOW CAN I MUNCH IN FRONT OF HER?

SPEAK TO ME, CHILD. SPEAK!

BUT MY MOUTH'S FULL.

HE CAN'T SPEAK! AND LOOK— HIS CHEEKS ARE SWOLLEN...

...HELP! HELP! HE'S SERIOUSLY ILL. GET A DOCTOR.

MOTHER, WAIT, I'LL CURE HIM FOR YOU.

LET ME DIAGNOSE HIS CONDITION, FIRST.

OH, GOD! HE HAS TUMOURS IN HIS CHEEKS!

WHAT!

O GOOD BARBER, CURE HIM AND I'LL GIVE YOU THE COW I KEPT SPECIALLY FOR MY SON-IN-LAW.

HMM...! MY SHAVING SCALPELS ARE SHARP ENOUGH FOR THE JOB.

33

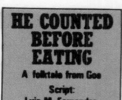

HE COUNTED BEFORE EATING

A folktale from Goa

Script:
Luis M. Fernandes

Illustrations:
Ram Waeerkar

A SON-IN-LAW ON A VISIT TO HIS WIFE'S HOUSE HAD JUST AWAKENED FROM HIS AFTERNOON SIESTA.

I COULD DO WITH SOME TEA NOW.

SAOANSOAN....!

OH, THEY'RE FRYING SANNAS!*

MMM... I CAN HARDLY WAIT TO EAT THEM.

SOAONSANN

THAT'S TWO! I'LL COUNT HOW MANY THEY MAKE.

THEY MUST BE TAKING IT OUT OF THE PAN NOW.

SOAONSOANN!

THAT'S THREE.

IN THE KITCHEN—

IT'S DONE ON THAT SIDE. TURN IT OVER.

* A GOAN DELICACY MADE OF RICE FLOUR

THAT'S FOUR.

THE SON-IN-LAW DID NOT KNOW THAT HE WAS COUNTING EACH SANNA TWICE. AND FINALLY—

THEY HAVE MADE TEN. WONDERFUL!

AT TEA-TIME, THE WIFE'S YOUNGER BROTHER PUSHED IN TO GRAB A SANNA, BUT—

NOT NOW! PEDRO! LET YOUR BROTHER-IN-LAW EAT FIRST.

GO AND CALL HIM FOR TEA.

THE SON-IN-LAW CAME EAGERLY TO THE TABLE...

...AND BEGAN TO EAT.

DELICIOUS!

WHILE THE LITTLE BOY WATCHED FROM THE DOORWAY.

THAT'S ONE.

The Telephone

Script: Subba Rao
Illustrations: Anand Mande

GRAHAM BELL WAS WORKING WITH AN INSTRUMENT DESIGNED TO CARRY SOUND, IN HIS WORKSHOP IN BOSTON, AMERICA.

BY ACCIDENT HE SPILLED SOME BATTERY ACID ON HIS TROUSERS.

HE GOT UP AND CRIED OUT—

WATSON...

...PLEASE COME HERE. I WANT YOU!

WATSON, BELL'S ASSISTANT, WORKING IN ANOTHER ROOM ON THE FIRST FLOOR, WAS STUNNED BECAUSE HIS EMPLOYER'S VOICE HAD COME THROUGH THE INSTRUMENT!

HE RAN DOWN THE STAIRS...

...AND BURST INTO BELL'S ROOM.

IT WORKS! IT WORKS!

THE ERA OF THE TELEPHONE HAD BEGUN. THE YEAR WAS 1876.

37

IN THE EARLY MODELS THE SAME TUBE SERVED AS THE MOUTHPIECE AND THE EARPIECE. ANYONE USING THE TELEPHONE HAD TO BE EXTREMELY AGILE, MOVING HIS EAR AND MOUTH TO THE INSTRUMENT TO HEAR AND SPEAK ALTERNATELY.
ONE MODEL CARRIED THE NOTICE:
"DO NOT LISTEN WITH YOUR MOUTH AND TALK WITH YOUR EAR."

IN LATER MODELS, THE EARPIECE AND THE MOUTHPIECE WERE SEPARATED BUT ONE HAD TO SHOUT TO MAKE ONESELF HEARD ON THE TELEPHONE...

...TILL DAVID HUGHES CAME UP WITH THE MICROPHONE, AND IT WAS COMBINED WITH THE LISTENING TUBE.

HERE ARE PICTURES OF VARIOUS MODELS OF THE TELEPHONE DEVELOPED OVER THE YEARS.

ON NOVEMBER 18, 1881 AT THE BANDSTAND ON THE SOUTH BEACH, MADRAS, THE GOVERNOR'S BAND PLAYED A VARIETY OF PIECES...

...WHICH A NUMBER OF PEOPLE LISTENED TO WITH DELIGHT AT THE MESS HOUSE AT FORT ST GEORGE.

THE TELEPHONE HAD ARRIVED IN INDIA!

HOWEVER, IT WAS ONLY IN 1950, THREE YEARS AFTER THE COUNTRY BECAME INDEPENDENT THAT TELEPHONE INSTRUMENTS AND OTHER EQUIPMENT BEGAN TO BE MANUFACTURED IN INDIA AT INDIAN TELEPHONE INDUSTRIES, BANGALORE.

IT IS NOW A MASSIVE INDUSTRIAL COMPLEX WITH OVER 25,000 EMPLOYEES WORKING IN FACTORIES IN BANGALORE, NAINI, SRINAGAR, RAE BARELI AND PALGHAT.

We are grateful to Indian Telephone Industries. Bangalore for providing us with pictorial references
—Editor

ANWAR

by
Appaswami

Illustrations: V. B. Halbe

40

41

42

THE AMAZON-I

Script : Vaijayanti Wagle
Illustrations : Ajit Vasaikar

IN THE YEAR 1500, THE SPANISH CAPTAIN VINCENT YANEZ PINZON WAS EXPLORING THE EAST COAST OF SOUTH AMERICA SUDDENLY—

AHOY, CAPTAIN! WE ARE SAILING THROUGH FRESH WATER.

WHY THAT'S IMPOSSIBLE WE ARE 120 MILES OUT AT SEA.

A BUCKET WAS LOWERED TO SAMPLE THE WATER

STRANGE! THIS IS INDEED FRESH WATER.

TURN THE SHIP AROUND. WE MUST UNRAVEL THIS MYSTERY.

AS THE SHIP CHANGED ITS COURSE, PINZON AND HIS CREW FOUND THEMSELVES SURROUNDED BY FRESH WATER OVER AN AREA OF 64 KM.

AMAZING! THIS MUST BE A FRESH-WATER SEA. I WILL CALL IT 'LA MER DULCE'.

BUT AS THEY EXPLORED FURTHER—

BY THE GOD ALMIGHTY, THIS IS NOT A SEA AT ALL. WE ARE IN THE MIDST OF A GIGANTIC RIVER.

WHAT HE WAS NEVER TO KNOW WAS THAT HE HAD DISCOVERED ONLY A SMALL PART OF THE AMAZON, THE WORLD'S LARGEST RIVER.

STRANGELY ENOUGH THIS MIGHTY RIVER BEGINS AS A SMALL BROOK 5600 M. HIGH IN THE SNOW-CAPPED ANDES MOUNTAINS OF PERU. FROM HERE IT PLUNGES DOWN RAVINES AND GORGES AND FLOWS THROUGH COLUMBIA AND BRAZIL TO EMPTY ITSELF OUT IN THE ATLANTIC OCEAN, 6400 KM. AWAY.

COLOMBIA

NORTH ATLANTIC OCEAN

AMAZON RIVER

BRAZIL

PERU

SOUTH PACIFIC OCEAN

ALONG THE WAY THE MAIN TRUNK OF THE RIVER IS JOINED BY 1,100 TRIBUTARIES.

ALL THE WATER THE AMAZON AND ITS TRIBUTARIES HAVE COLLECTED POURS OUT INTO THE ATLANTIC OCEAN. THE WATER POURED OUT INTO THE OCEAN AMOUNTS TO ONE-FIFTH OF ALL THE RIVER WATERS ON EARTH.

SO GREAT IS THE TORRENT OF WATER THAT FLOWS OUT INTO THE ATLANTIC THAT IT PUSHES BACK THE SALT WATER OF THE OCEAN OVER 760 KM., WHICH IS WHY PINZON AND HIS CREW THOUGHT THEY HAD SAILED INTO A FRESH-WATER SEA.

44

WHERE DOES ALL THIS WATER COME FROM? SOME OF IT COMES FROM THE MELTING SNOWS OF THE ANDES MOUNTAINS.

MUCH OF THE WATER IN THE RIVER AND ITS TRIBUTARIES IS COLLECTED FROM THE RAIN THAT FALLS HERE. AND IT IS ALWAYS RAINING HERE.

IT IS EXTREMELY HOT IN THE AMAZON BASIN. THE INTENSE HEAT CAUSES WATER TO EVAPORATE. THE RESULTING WATER VAPOUR RISES HIGH AND AS IT REACHES THE COOL LAYERS ABOVE, IT FORMS BIG RAIN CLOUDS.

EVERY AFTERNOON, THE SKY DARKENS WITH THICK CLOUDS, LIGHTNING CRACKLES THROUGH THE SKY AND THE THUNDER ROLLS. SOON THE RAIN POURS DOWN IN GREAT SHEETS OF WATER.

THE AMAZON, ITS TRIBUTARIES AND THE JUNGLES AROUND THEM, COMPRISE A HUGE WILDERNESS SPREAD OUT OVER NINE SOUTH AMERICAN COUNTRIES.

AMAZON-II

Script : Vaijayanti Wagle
Illustrations : Ajit Vasaikar

THE AMAZON RIVER FLOWS THROUGH VERY THICK JUNGLE. IT IS SO DARK AND FORBIDDING THAT IT IS ALMOST UNTOUCHED BY MAN. STRANGE INSECTS, BIRDS, ANIMALS AND PLANTS ARE FOUND HERE.

THERE IS THE CANNONBALL TREE. ITS FRUIT IS AS HARD AS IRON AND WHEN IT FALLS TO THE GROUND IT MAKES A VERY LOUD SOUND.

THE AMAZONIAN VICTORIA LILY HAS HUGE LEAVES THAT LOOK LIKE GIANT-SIZED PLATES.

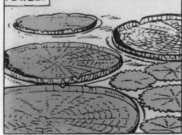

THE ANACONDA IS THE LARGEST SNAKE IN THE WORLD, OFTEN GROWING TO OVER 10 METRES. IT WRAPS ITSELF ROUND ITS VICTIM, SUFFOCATING IT AND THEN SWALLOWS IT WHOLE.

THERE ARE A WIDE VARIETY OF MONKEYS, HAPPILY JUMPING FROM TREE TO TREE.

A WOOLLY MONKEY

THE NOCTURNAL DOUROUCOOLIS

A HOWLER MONKEY

THE CAPYBARAS IS THE WORLD'S LARGEST RODENT, ALTHOUGH IT LOOKS LIKE A FIRST COUSIN OF THE PIG'S. IT CAN GROW UPTO 1¼ METRES AND WEIGHS ABOUT 73 KGS. IT HAS WEBBED FEET AND IS A VERY GOOD SWIMMER.

BECAUSE OF THE THICK VEGETATION VERY LARGE ANIMALS ARE RARE. SO IT IS THE INSECTS THAT RULE THE JUNGLE. ANTS CROWD INTO EVERY AVAILABLE SPACE. FIRE ANTS EAT EVERYTHING IN SIGHT. LEAF-EATING SAUVA ANTS CAN DESTROY GARDENS OVERNIGHT.

AND CARNIVOROUS ARMY ANTS CAN TURN A CADAVER INTO A SKELETON WITHIN MINUTES.

THE BIRD-EATING SPIDER HAS A 17½ CM. LEG SPAN. IT RUNS AND POUNCES ON ITS PREY. ITS BITE IS FATAL TO SMALL BIRDS AND INSECTS.

THOUSANDS OF SPECIES OF BUTTERFLIES FLIT THROUGH THE GLOOMY JUNGLE IN THEIR GLITTERING COLOURS.

THE RIVER WATERS ARE TEEMING WITH OVER 1500 VARIETIES OF FISH. THE DEADLY PIRANHA ARE TINY FISH THAT TRAVEL IN LARGE SCHOOLS. THEY CAN EAT A MAN OR ANIMAL TO THE BONE IN A MATTER OF MINUTES.

AND THE AMAZON BASIN IS THE HOME OF MORE THAN HALF OF THE 8,600 SPECIES OF THE BIRDS IN THE WORLD.

HUMMING BIRD

MACAW

SCARLET IBIS

TOUCAN

HOATZIN

THE CLEVER COURT JESTER

Illustrations: V. B. Halbe

Readers' Choice

Based on a story sent by N. R. Shripathi, New Mangalore

ONE DAY A SCHOLAR FROM ANOTHER COUNTRY CAME TO THE COURT OF A KING.

I CHALLENGE ANYONE HERE TO DEFEAT ME IN A BATTLE OF WITS!

A BATTLE OF WITS? I....UH... AM SURE WE CAN FIND SOMEONE TO TAKE UP YOUR CHALLENGE.

IF ANYONE DEFEATS YOU, YOU WILL PRESENT HIM WITH THIS NECKLACE. IF NOT, YOU WILL KEEP IT FOR YOURSELF.

BUT NO ONE AT THE COURT COULD DEFEAT THE MAN. AND FINALLY—

MY FRIEND, IT LOOKS AS IF YOU'VE WON!

BUT A VOICE RANG OUT—

NO! I WOULD LIKE A CHANCE AS WELL!

IT WAS THE KING'S JESTER.

NOW, I WILL ASK YOU FIVE QUESTIONS, TO ALL OF WHICH YOU MUST GIVE ME AN INCORRECT ANSWER...

50

YOU ARE WEARING A GOLD NECKLACE, AREN'T YOU?

NO!

REALLY, YOU ARE VERY CLEVER! HOW MANY QUESTIONS HAVE I ASKED SO FAR?

FOUR! YOU HAVE JUST ONE MORE TO GO! HA! HA!

I HAVE JUST ASKED IT! AND YOU HAVE ANSWERED IT CORRECTLY.

HE HAS LOST TO OUR JESTER!

I ACCEPT DEFEAT! HERE IS THE CHAIN!

O KING, I CAN SEE THAT YOUR DAYS CAN NEVER BE DULL WITH SUCH A JESTER BY YOUR SIDE!

51

MEET THE COW

Script: Ashvin
Illustrations : Ajit Vasaikar

CATTLE HAVE BEEN DOMESTICATED FOR THOUSANDS OF YEARS. COWS HAVE BEEN REARED FOR THEIR MILK AND THE MALES (BULLS OR OXEN) HAVE BEEN USED TO PULL HEAVY LOADS.

IND AN COWS HAVE A HUMP AND A LARGE DEWLAP. THE DEWLAP IS THE FOLD OF SKIN HANGING DOWN FROM THEIR NECKS. THE COW LOSES EXCESS HEAT IN ITS BODY THROUGH THE DEWLAP.

A COW STARTS GIVING MILK ONLY WHEN IT HAS GIVEN BIRTH TO A CALF. AND THEN IT CONTINUES TO GIVE MILK FOR NINE TO TEN MONTHS AFTERWARDS. INDIAN COWS GIVE FIVE TO SIX LITRES OF MILK A DAY.

EUROPEAN BREEDS GIVE UPTO FIFTY LITRES OF MILK A DAY. THESE COWS ARE RAISED ESPECIALLY FOR THEIR MILK.

IF YOU LOOK AT A JERSEY COW, FOR EXAMPLE, YOU'LL SEE THAT HER UDDERS ARE SO LARGE THAT SHE CAN HARDLY WALK. JERSEY COWS, HOWEVER, PRODUCE THE RICHEST MILK.

COWS BEING MILKED BY MACHINE AT A DAIRY FARM IN EUROPE

THE PROTEIN CONTENT OF MILK IS HIGHEST FOR GUERNSEY COWS (3·91 PERCENT).

THE MILK IS PRODUCED BY THE COW FROM HER BLOOD.
EACH TIME BLOOD PASSES THROUGH THE UDDER, SOME PART OF THE BLOOD IS CHANGED INTO MILK. ABOUT 200 LITRES OF BLOOD MUST PASS THROUGH THE UDDER TO MAKE ABOUT 450 GMS. OF MILK.

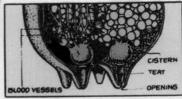

CISTERN
TEAT
OPENING
BLOOD VESSELS

SO IF A COW IS TO GIVE A LOT OF MILK, IT MUST GET A LOT OF FOOD. IN INDIA, THE COW IS FED GRAINS, BRAN AND OILCAKES IN ADDITION TO GRASS AND HAY.

EUROPE, THE U.S.A., NEW ZEALAND AND AUSTRALIA HAVE RICH GRASSLANDS AND A CLIMATE IN WHICH COWS THRIVE.
SO THEY ARE THE LARGEST MILK-PRODUCING COUNTRIES.

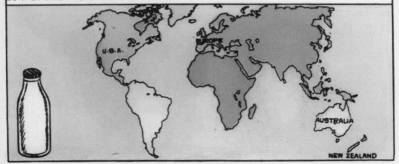

U.S.A.
EUROPE
AUSTRALIA
NEW ZEALAND

THE COW SWALLOWS ITS FOOD QUICKLY AND STORES IT IN THE PAUNCH OR RUMEN, THE FIRST OF THE FOUR COMPARTMENTS OF ITS STOMACH. LATER THE FOOD PASSES INTO THE SECOND COMPARTMENT, THE RETICULUM WHERE IT IS ROLLED INTO LITTLE BALLS OR CUDS.

WHEN THE ANIMAL IS RESTING, IT BRINGS UP THESE CUDS, CHEWS THEM MORE THOROUGHLY AND SWALLOWS THEM AGAIN.

THIS TIME THE FOOD PASSES INTO THE THIRD AND THEN INTO THE FOURTH COMPARTMENTS – THE OMASUM AND THE ABOMASUM.
DIGESTION TAKES PLACE IN THE ABOMASUM.

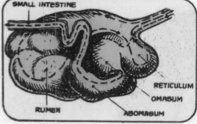

SMALL INTESTINE

RETICULUM

OMASUM

RUMEN

ABOMASUM

SOME EUROPEAN CATTLE LIKE THE HEREFORD COW SHOWN HERE, ARE RAISED FOR THEIR MEAT.
THESE CATTLE HAVE HEAVY WELL-ROUNDED BODIES.

WATUSSI CATTLE, BRED IN UGANDA, HAVE THE LARGEST HORNS OF ALL DOMESTIC CATTLE.

The Wonder of Wonders

A Folktale from Bihar

Script
Meera Ugra

Illustrations:
Ram Waeerkar

POORAN PANDE, THE JESTER, ENTERTAINED THE KING WITH FUNNY STORIES AND EARNED MANY REWARDS...

...AND ENEMIES, TOO!

WE WORK SO HARD...

...AND HE REAPS THE REWARDS! HUH!

WE MUST SHOW THE KING HE IS WORTHLESS. LISTEN...

THE NEXT DAY—

MAHARAJ! MAHARAJ!

WHAT IS THE MATTER, MINISTER?

MAHARAJ... WE ARE DOOMED... GODDESS DURGA HERSELF TOLD ME... IN A DREAM...

!?

...THAT UNLESS... UNLESS WE PROCURE THE WONDER OF WONDERS AND INSTALL IT IN HER TEMPLE...

WONDER OF WONDERS? WHAT IS THAT?

PERHAPS POORAN PANDE WILL KNOW.

AND BE ABLE TO GET IT FOR US, TOO.

WELL, POORAN! WHAT DO YOU THINK? CAN YOU GET THE WONDER OF WONDERS — WHATEVER IT IS?

YES, MAHARAJ BUT YOU MUST ALLOW ME ONE MONTH...

ANOTHER PLOT TO OUTWIT ME... HMM.

...AND I WILL NEED SOME MONEY, TOO.

OF COURSE, POORAN.

A MONTH LATER, POORAN WENT TO THE MINISTER'S HOUSE.

WELCOME! WELCOME! HAVE YOU BEEN SUCCESSFUL, POORAN?

I HAVE, SIR. BUT I NEED YOUR HELP

PLEASE COME TO MY HOUSE AND TELL ME IF IT'S THE CREATURE WHICH THE GODDESS DESIRED.

I'LL COME, POORAN.

THE TWO SET OFF.

I'LL GO AND SAY IT'S THE WRONG CREATURE ...THE KING WILL BE FURIOUS! HEE HEE HEE!

I DO HOPE IT'S THE RIGHT THING...

56

...THE AMOUNT OF TROUBLE I TOOK TO GET IT!

PLEASE COME IN.

WHERE HAVE YOU KEPT IT, POORAN?

I HAVE LOCKED IT AWAY. BUT DON'T WORRY, SIR! FIRST PLEASE HAVE SOME REFRESHMENTS.

WIFE! OUR HONOURED GUEST IS HERE!

POORAN'S WIFE SOON APPEARED.

COME THIS WAY, SIR AND WASH YOUR HANDS.

UH... OH... YES, YES!

HALWA! PURIS! JALEBIS! AHA!

SIRRR

57

OOOPS!

EH?

I'M... I'M... SO SORRY, SIR!

...WHAT'S THIS STICKY MESS, POORAN?

IT IS... ER... A SYRUP OF GUR, SIR.

BUT YOU MUST WASH, SIR. THE BATHROOM IS OVER HERE.

AS THE MINISTER STEPPED INTO THE ROOM, A BASKET OF COTTON WAS WAITING FOR HIM...

AAAH!

WH... WHAT IS HAPPENING?

...AND MORE COTTON—

Ouiiee!!

CLANG!!

BANG! BANG!

POORAN! OPEN THE DOOR!

IN A SHORT WHILE, SIR!

POORAN RUSHED TO THE COURT.

POORAN! YOU? AND WHERE IS THE WONDER OF WONDERS?

AT HOME, MAHARAJ...

...THE CREATURE IS SO ANGRY AT THE MOMENT, IT'S DIFFICULT TO CONTROL IT. PLEASE COME TO MY HOUSE TO SEE IT.

WELL... I'LL COME. BUT WHERE IS THE MINISTER?

HE HASN'T COME TODAY, MAHARAJ.

WHAT A PITY! HE'LL MISS A RARE SIGHT. LET'S GO.

WHEN THE PARTY ARRIVED AT POORAN PANDE'S HOUSE—

BANG! BANG!

DIDN'T I TELL YOU IT'S FURIOUS!

HERE'S THE WONDER OF WONDERS, MAHARAJ.

YOU! YOU! ...OH!

WATCH OUT, POORAN!

GUARDS! HOLD HIM! TAKE HIM TO THE PALACE.

MAHARAJ!! MAHARAJ!!

MINISTER! I'M GLAD YOU'VE COME ...BUT WHERE ARE YOU?

I'M HERE, MAHARAJ. I'M THE WONDER OF WONDERS.

!?

I'LL EXPLAIN ALL, MAHARAJ...

THE KING WAS AMUSED WITH HIS STORY AND REWARDED POORAN PANDE HANDSOMELY. AND THE JEALOUS COURTIERS NEVER TROUBLED HIM AGAIN.

60

Script : J.D. Isloor

Illustrations :
Anand Mande

IF A FOREIGNER WERE ASKED ABOUT THE CLIMATE OF OUR COUNTRY, HE WOULD SAY IT IS WARM, AND HE WOULD BE RIGHT. BECAUSE EVEN THOUGH THE WEATHER HERE CAN BE COLD DURING WINTER AND DAMP DURING THE MONSOONS, THE GREATER PART OF INDIA IS GENERALLY WARM THROUGHOUT THE YEAR. THE CLIMATE OF ANY COUNTRY IS THE GENERAL WEATHER OF THAT COUNTRY.

THE CLIMATE OF A PLACE HAS A GREAT DEAL TO DO WITH HOW THE PEOPLE OF THE REGION LIVE. WHAT THEY EAT AND WHAT THEY WEAR DEPEND PARTLY ON THE CLIMATE.

IN INDIA WE WEAR LIGHT COTTON CLOTHES. OUR FOOD IS MAINLY VEGETARIAN. AND OUR HOUSES ARE WELL VENTILATED.

EUROPEANS LIVE DIFFERENTLY.
THE SUN SHINES MILDLY ON THEIR COUNTRIES.
AND THE WINTERS ARE LONG. SO THEIR
HOUSES HAVE TO BE ARTIFICIALLY HEATED.
AND THEIR CLOTHING IS HEAVY AND WARM.
MEAT IS AN IMPORTANT PART OF THEIR DIET.

ESKIMOS LIVE IN A STILL COLDER CLIMATE.
THEIR HOUSES (IGLOOS) ARE BUILT OUT
OF SNOW. AS CROPS CANNOT GROW ON
THEIR LAND, THE ESKIMOS LIVE MAINLY
ON FOOD FROM THE SEA INCLUDING FISH
AND SEALS. THEIR CLOTHING IS MADE OUT
OF ANIMAL SKINS.

THE CHIEF FACTOR IN CLIMATE IS THE
AMOUNT OF HEAT RECEIVED FROM THE
SUN. THE EARTH IS SURROUNDED BY THE
LAYER OF GAS THAT WE BREATHE AND
WHICH WE CALL THE ATMOSPHERE. BEFORE
SUNLIGHT REACHES THE SURFACE OF THE
EARTH, IT HAS TO PASS THROUGH THE
ATMOSPHERE WHICH REFLECTS ABOUT HALF
THE HEAT BACK INTO SPACE.

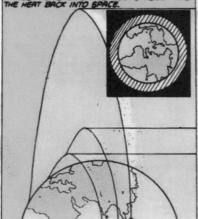

BECAUSE OF THE CURVATURE OF THE EARTH,
THE RAYS OF THE SUN HIT THE EARTH AT
DIFFERENT ANGLES.
THE RAYS ARE DIRECT AT THE EQUATOR.
SO THIS IS THE HOTTEST REGION. AT THE
POLES A SIMILAR AMOUNT OF RAYS
SPREAD OVER A LARGER DISTANCE. SO
THIS REGION RECEIVES MUCH LESS HEAT.

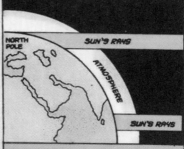

YOU CAN ALSO SEE FROM THE FIGURE
THAT THE SUN'S RAYS TRAVEL A GREATER
DISTANCE THROUGH THE ATMOSPHERE
AT THE POLAR REGION THAN AT THE
EQUATOR. BECAUSE OF THIS, THE RAYS
LOSE A LOT OF HEAT BEFORE THEY
REACH THE GROUND AT THE POLES.

OCEANS ALSO CONTRIBUTE TO THE CLIMATE OF A PLACE. LAND HEATS UP FASTER THAN WATER. LAND COOLS FASTER TOO. LONG AFTER THE LAND HAS COOLED THE WATER IS STILL VERY WARM. THIS IS WHY, IN WINTER, PLACES NEAR THE SEA, LIKE BOMBAY AND GOA ARE MUCH WARMER THAN PLACES IN THE INTERIOR LIKE NAGPUR AND AHMEDABAD.

IN SUMMER, THE HOT SUN QUICKLY HEATS UP THE LAND BUT THE WATER OF THE OCEAN TAKES TIME TO GET HEATED. AS A RESULT THE SEA IS COOLER THAN THE LAND AND PLACES NEAR THE SEA ARE COOLER THAN PLACES IN THE INTERIOR.

ALTITUDE ALSO AFFECTS CLIMATE. THE AIR IS THINNER AT HIGHER ALTITUDES AND THE TEMPERATURE DROPS ABOUT ½ °C FOR EVERY 92 METRES UP.
MOUNT CHIMBORAZO IN ECUADOR, IN SOUTH AMERICA IS ON THE EQUATOR, BUT IT HAS A PERMANENT CAP OF SNOW.

THE WATER IS NOT EVEN WARM!... NEVER MIND. WISE MEN NEVER GIVE UP!

SO —

AND THEN —

SPLASH

!!

HISSS!

WHAT A STUPID FIRE!

SUPPANDI!

HAVE YOU...OH, MY GOD! WHAT'S ALL THIS?

IT'S NOT MY FAULT, SIR. THIS FIRE IS MOST PECULIAR. IT MELTS OUT OF FEAR EVERYTIME I THROW THE WATER ON IT!

A TALE FROM GOA

Illustrations: Ram Waeerkar

Based on a story sent by Renuka Dennis, Goa

SANTAN, A FARMER, AND HIS SON, MIGUEL WERE GOING TO A DISTANT VILLAGE.

NIGHT FELL AS THEY WERE PASSING THROUGH A FOREST.

LET US FIND A PLACE TO SLEEP.

THIS IS A GOOD SPOT.

SOMETIME LATER—

I DON'T LIKE SLEEPING ON THIS SIDE OF YOU.

COME TO THIS SIDE, THEN.

FATHER, I DON'T LIKE THIS SIDE EITHER. I WANT TO SLEEP IN THE MIDDLE.

MIDDLE?

66

OH, ALL RIGHT...

WAGN, THE TIGER WAS ON THE PROWL.

I CAN SMELL A MAN.

AH, HERE HE IS.

BUT I SEE FOUR LEGS. MAN HAS TWO.

WHAT STRANGE CREATURE IS THIS? I WILL ASK MANGEM, THE CROCODILE!

67

68

69

PRINCE ABHAYA

Story:
Motilal Surana

Illustrations:
Ram Waeerkar

PRINCE ABHAYA WAS ON A VISIT TO HIS UNCLE, THE KING OF SUMERPUR. THE KING WAS A LOVER OF SPORT—

...AND YOUR ARROW MUST PIERCE THE EYE OF THAT CLAY BIRD.

THE FIRST ARCHER MISSED...

...SO DID THE SECOND...

...AND THE REST OF THEM.

MAY I DISPLAY MY SKILL, UNCLE?

WHY NOT, ABHAYA.

ABHAYA STRUNG THE BOW...

...AND—

SNICK

THAT WAS GREAT ABHAYA, MY BOY.

O, THANK YOU, UNCLE.

THE CHILDLESS KING WAS FULL OF JOY.

70

THAT NIGHT—

I WISH I HAD A SON LIKE ABHAYA—HE'S SO SKILLED.

WHY DON'T WE ADOPT HIM, THEN?

YES, BUT I MUST TEST HIM FURTHER.

THE NEXT DAY—

OH, OH!

WE'LL GET IT OUT IMMEDIATELY, UNCLE.

THE KING'S RING HAD SLIPPED AND FALLEN INTO A DITCH.

WAIT A MINUTE, ABHAYA. CAN YOU TAKE THAT RING OUT WITHOUT ENTERING THAT DITCH?

HMM! GIVE ME A FEW DAYS, UNCLE.

TAKE AS MUCH TIME AS YOU LIKE.

ABHAYA GET TO WORK—

GANGURAM! MIX SOME COWDUNG WITH HAY.

YES, SIR.

SOMETIME LATER—

IT'S READY, SIR.

GOOD. NOW THROW IT INTO THE DITCH, SLOWLY...

...JUST ON THAT RING.

SPLAT

MORE

SPLAT

STILL MORE!

THERE! NOW LEAVE IT TO DRY AND HARDEN. THEN WE WILL BRING IT UP WITH A ROPE.

A FEW DAYS LATER—

TODAY, YOU'LL GET YOUR RING BACK, UNCLE.

AHA! LET ME SEE HOW YOU DO IT.

THEY APPROACHED THE DITCH—

OKAY GANGURAM, START.

NOW, BREAK THE CAKE.

HERE, UNCLE— YOUR RING.

GOOD BOY, ABHAYA.

BUT YOU HAVE ONE MORE TEST COMING UP, SON.

JUST THEN —

SALUTATIONS, MAHARAJ, PRINCE ABHAYA!

WHAT DO YOU WANT?

I'VE COME TO GET MY EYE BACK, PRINCE. HERE'S THE MONEY.

Y—YOUR EYE?

YES, MY OTHER EYE WHICH I HAD MORTGAGED WITH YOU LAST MONTH WHEN YOU'D LOANED ME THIS MONEY.

LOAN?

EYE...? LOAN...? OF COURSE, OF COURSE!

MY UNCLE SEEMS DETERMINED TO TEST ME.

LET ME COUNT THE MONEY FIRST...

OH, IT'S CORRECT TO THE LAST PAISA.

OH, ALL RIGHT. NOW WILL YOU LET ME HAVE YOUR OTHER EYE?

MY OTHER EYE... WHY?

I HAVE MANY EYES WITH ME. HOW CAN I MATCH YOURS UNLESS I HAVE YOUR OTHER EYE?

NE...NEVER MIND...HEY... I JUST REMEMBERED, I'M LATE FOR WORK.

HMM! HE'S QUICK-WITTED, TOO!

YOU HANDLED THAT WELL!

74

THE NEXT DAY —

ABHAYA, PLEASE DELIVER THIS PERSONAL LETTER TO THE KING OF JANAKPUR.

WITH PLEASURE, UNCLE.

THIS MUST BE ANOTHER TEST.

AT JANAKPUR —

FROM THE KING OF SUMER-PUR, YOUR MAJESTY.

GUARDS! GET THE EXECUTIONER THIS MAN MUST BE BEHEADED TODAY!

WAIT A MINUTE, YOUR MAJESTY.

IF YOU CARE FOR THE WELFARE OF YOUR PEOPLE... YOU WON'T EXECUTE ME HERE.

WHY?

FOR IT IS ORDAINED THAT IN THE LAND WHERE I DIE, THERE WILL BE A FAMINE FOR TEN YEARS...

WHAT?

75

AND THAT'S WHY THE KING OF SUMERPUR SENT ME TO DIE—HERE!

I SEE.

GUARDS!

THROW THIS MAN OUT OF OUR BORDERS... BUT CAREFULLY... SEE THAT YOU DON'T HURT HIM!

AT SUMERPUR—

I'M BACK, UNCLE.

HOW WAS YOUR TRIP?

OH, THE KING WAS VERY HOSPITABLE!

INDEED! I KNEW YOU WOULD RETURN SAFELY.

AND SO THE NEXT DAY—

I PROCLAIM YOU, ABHAYA, CROWN PRINCE OF SUMERPUR.

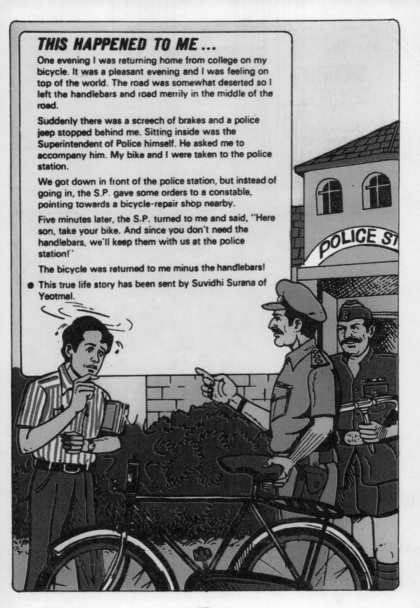

THIS HAPPENED TO ME ...

One evening I was returning home from college on my bicycle. It was a pleasant evening and I was feeling on top of the world. The road was somewhat deserted so I left the handlebars and road merrily in the middle of the road.

Suddenly there was a screech of brakes and a police jeep stopped behind me. Sitting inside was the Superintendent of Police himself. He asked me to accompany him. My bike and I were taken to the police station.

We got down in front of the police station, but instead of going in, the S.P. gave some orders to a constable, pointing towards a bicycle-repair shop nearby.

Five minutes later, the S.P. turned to me and said, "Here son, take your bike. And since you don't need the handlebars, we'll keep them with us at the police station!"

The bicycle was returned to me minus the handlebars!

● This true life story has been sent by Suvidhi Surana of Yeotmal.

POLICE ST

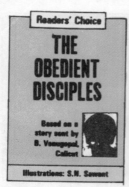

Readers' Choice

THE OBEDIENT DISCIPLES

Based on a story sent by B. Venugopal, Calicut

Illustrations: S.N. Sawant

ONCE UPON A TIME, THERE LIVED A SAGE WHO HAD MANY YOUNG DISCIPLES.

THE SAGE WAS RATHER VAIN.

FOLD YOUR HANDS WHENEVER YOU SEE ME.

ONE DAY THE SAGE AND HIS DISCIPLES WENT FOR A WALK.

SUDDENLY —

ANWAR

by
Appaswami

Illustrations: V. B. Halbe

VIDYA, GIVE ME A TOFFEE!

SAY "PLEASE".

PLEASE?

OH, YOU WILL NEVER UNDERSTAND.

AREN'T YOU GOING TO GIVE ME A TOFFEE?

I WILL, IF YOU ASK IN THE CORRECT WAY.

COME, I WILL TEACH YOU.

HERE, TAKE THESE.

ALL THE TOFFEES? WOW!

NOW WATCH ME ASK YOU...

ANWAR, COULD YOU GIVE ME A TOFFEE, PLEASE?

CERTAINLY NOT. I WANT THEM ALL!

80

THE FOOLISH WEAVER

Script: Gayatri Madan Dutt
Illustrations: V.B. Halbe

THERE WAS ONCE A WEAVER WHO WAS FOND OF SHOWING OFF. ONE DAY, AS HE WAS PREPARING TO LEAVE FOR HIS FATHER-IN-LAW'S VILLAGE, A THOUGHT STRUCK HIM.

IF I LOOKED RICH AND IMPRESSIVE, EVERYONE WOULD ENVY MY FATHER-IN-LAW FOR HAVING GOT HOLD OF SUCH A FINE SON-IN-LAW!

AND SO—

FRIEND, COULD I BORROW YOUR MARE FOR A FEW DAYS?

WELL... ALL RIGHT. BUT DO TAKE CARE OF IT.

FRIEND, COULD I BORROW YOUR JEWELS AND CLOTHES FOR A WHILE?

ALL RIGHT— BUT BE CAREFUL WITH THEM.

SOON—

HE, HE, HE! EVERYONE'S GAZING AT ME WITH SUCH ADMIRATION!

81

SUDDENLY, ON THE WAY —

OH, NO—
A STORM!

RUMBLE

I WILL HAVE TO WAIT AT THIS VILLAGE TILL IT CLEARS. WHAT A NUISANCE!

THE STORM RAGED FOR A LONG TIME. IT WAS LATE EVENING BY THE TIME THE WEAVER COULD CONTINUE HIS JOURNEY.

HERE'S FATHER-IN-LAW'S VILLAGE AT LAST, AND NOT A SOUL ABOUT!

IF I ENTER NOW, NOBODY WILL SEE ME ALL DRESSED UP. I'D RATHER MAKE A GRAND ENTRANCE IN THE MORNING.

SEEING A HUT NEARBY, THE WEAVER WENT UP TO IT.

ANYBODY IN?

KNOCK KNOCK

WHAT DO YOU WANT?

GREETINGS, GOOD FAKIR. I AM JUST A TRAVELLER WANTING SHELTER FOR THE NIGHT.

GO AWAY! HOW DO I KNOW WHO YOU MAY BE? WHAT... WHAT IF YOU ARE A THIEF, COME TO ROB A POOR FAKIR?

OH, SIR! YOU ARE QUITE MISTAKEN. HOW CAN I PROVE MY GOOD FAITH TO YOU?

WELL... DO THIS FOR ME, THEN...

... I AM OLD AND FIND IT DIFFICULT TO GO AND ASK FOR ALMS EVERYDAY. IF YOU WEAR MY CLOTHES AND GO TODAY IN MY STEAD, YOU CAN STAY HERE.

BUT... HOW CAN I...?

THEN, I'M SORRY...

ALL RIGHT, ALL RIGHT... I'LL GO, BUT WHAT ABOUT MY MARE AND MY CLOTHES?

LEAVE THEM HERE. THEY WILL BE SAFE WITH ME.

83

SO, DRESSED IN THE FAKIR'S TATTERS, THE WEAVER SET OUT.

SEEK ALMS AT EVERY HOUSE. I HAVE TAKEN A VOW TO HONOUR EVERY HOUSE BY EATING WHAT EACH OFFERS.

I CAN RECOGNISE THE FOOD FROM EVERY HOUSE, SO BE SURE TO DO AS I SAY.

THEN I'LL HAVE TO GO TO MY FATHER-IN-LAW'S HOUSE ALSO!

SOON THE WEAVER ARRIVED AT HIS FATHER-IN-LAW'S.

OH, THE GRAIN PIT! IT'S FULL OF WATER FROM THIS MORNING'S STORM.

ALMS! ALMS FOR A FAKIR.

I'M COMING, SIR.

HELP! IT'S MY WIFE. SHE MUSN'T RECOGNISE ME...

...AAA...

...HAAH!

EEEE! FATHER, MOTHER— A FAKIR'S FALLEN INTO THE PIT!

NEIGHBOURS, NEIGHBOURS COME! SOMETHING'S HAPPENED NEXT DOOR.

WHAT IS IT?

GET A LIGHT SOMEONE.

84

SOON—
HE'S SAFE; QUITE SAFE.

HERE'S FIRE TO WARM HIM...

SON-IN-LAW! YOU!

I... C...C... CAN EXP-P-PLAIN...

CHATTER CHATTER

AND WHEN THE HAPLESS WEAVER NARRATED HIS WHOLE STORY—

A FAKIR, YOU SAY? BUT HE ARRIVED HERE JUST TWO DAYS AGO. I ONLY HOPE... HE IS...A REAL FAKIR...?

THEY ALL MADE HASTILY FOR THE FAKIR'S HUT.

THE MARE! THE CLOTHES, JEWELS! THE FAKIR — ALL GONE! WHAT WILL MY FRIENDS SAY?

HEAR FIRST WHAT I HAVE TO SAY...

...SO, YOU WANTED TO ENTER THE VILLAGE IN THE MORNING WHEN EVERYONE COULD SEE YOU, EH?... EVERYONE CAN SEE YOU NOW, FOOLISH ONE...

... AND WHAT A FINE SPECIMEN OF A SON-IN-LAW YOU MAKE!

A TAIL'S TALE

Illustrations: Ashok Dongre

Readers' Choice

Based on a story sent by
Rashmi Mishra, Khagadia, Bihar

ONE EVENING, IN SHEIKH INHAAM IBN MOOSA'S DESERT CAMP—

UNCLE! THE GOLD COINS HAVE BEEN STOLEN!

WHAT?

IT WAS BAAKAR, THE SHEIKH'S NEPHEW.

THE THIEF HAS GOT TO BE SOMEONE IN MY CAMP.

TELL THE MEN WHAT HAS HAPPENED AND SUMMON THEM AT ONCE, BAAKAR.

Y-YES, UNCLE.

WHEN THE MEN ASSEMBLED—

THIS MAGIC DONKEY WILL REVEAL THE THIEF TO ME.

HE LED THE DONKEY INTO A TENT.

EACH ONE OF YOU WILL GO IN AND HOLD THE DONKEY'S TAIL — THE DONKEY WILL BLURT OUT THE THIEF'S NAME WHEN THE THIEF HOLDS IT.

GO IN NOW... ONE BY ONE.

NEXT.

NEXT.

WHEN EVERYBODY WAS OUT—

SO THE DONKEY HAS FAILED TO CATCH THE THIEF...

NEVER MIND... I KNOW HOW TO READ PALMS. I'LL CATCH THE THIEF MYSELF.

HE READ THE FIRST MAN'S HAND...

...AND SNIFFED AT IT.

INNOCENT!

87

THEN THE SECOND...

INNOCENT.

...AND THE THIRD.

INNOCENT.

AND SO ON UNTIL THE SEVENTH.

SUDDENLY—

YOU ARE THE THIEF! DO YOU DENY THAT?

N...NO SIR, I... I... STOLE THE COINS.

THAT NIGHT—

HOW DID YOU CATCH THE RIGHT MAN, UNCLE?

OH, IT WAS SIMPLE...

I RUBBED A PASTE OF CAMPHOR AND MINT ON THE DONKEY'S TAIL. THE PALMS OF EVERY MAN WHO TOUCHED IT SMELT OF CAMPHOR.

BUT THE THIEF DIDN'T TOUCH THE TAIL...

...AND OF COURSE, HIS HANDS DIDN'T SMELL OF THE PASTE!

88

THE MOVING ARROW

You will need : A glass, water, a piece of card.

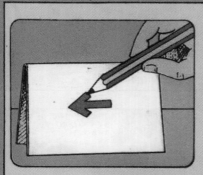

1 Fold a sheet of card in half and draw an arrow in the centre of one side.

2. Stand the card on a table and place an empty glass in front of the card. Now, can you change the direction of the arrow without touching the card ?

3. You can do so just by filling the glass with water !

THE THIEF IN THE TUB

Romantic Tales of the Punjab

Script: Anju Aggarwal
Illustrations: Ram Waeerkar

ONE DAY, A LITTLE BOY WAS PLAYING OUTSIDE HIS HOUSE. HE HAPPENED TO LOOK INTO A TUB OF WATER AND SAW HIS REFLECTION IN IT.

OH!

MOTHER! MOTHER!

MOTHER! THERE IS A CHILD IN THIS TUB...

... BEGGING FOR BREAD.

HUSBAND! COME HERE!

LOOK INTO THE TUB AND SEE IF ANYONE IS THERE.

WIFE, THERE IS NO CHILD HERE, BUT

90

... AN OLD VILLAIN, A THIEF.

GET INTO THE HOUSE QUICKLY.

THE MAN PICKED UP A STONE ...

...AND HURLED IT INTO THE TUB.

?

THERE'S NO ONE HERE.

CUNNING RASCAL— THAT THIEF...

...I DON'T KNOW HOW HE ESCAPED. BUT HE IS NOT LIKELY TO TROUBLE US AGAIN.

Kalia
THE CROW

Script:
PRASAD

Illustrations:
ASHOK DONGRE

THE FOREST IS CERTAINLY THICK HERE, CHAMATAKA.

HEH! HEH! THAT GIVES ME AN IDEA.

WHAT ARE THOSE TWO UP TO?

TIE THAT VINE TO THOSE TREES, DOOB DOOB. I'LL HIDE FURTHER UP THE TRACK...

... AND SEE IF I CAN DRIVE A DEER OR SOMETHING TOWARDS THIS PLACE.

WHEN I SHOUT "NOW!", LIFT THE VINE, SO THAT THE ANIMAL TRIPS.

WHAT A CLEVER IDEA, CHAMATAKA!

YES, VERY CLEVER! IT MIGHT EVEN WORK IF I DON'T DO SOMETHING ABOUT IT.

NOW TO FIND A GOOD HIDING PLACE.

THESE BUSHES WILL DO. IT WON'T BE LONG BEFORE SOME ANIMAL COMES THIS WAY.

SO THAT'S WHERE HE'S GOING TO HIDE!

ER...BABLOO. YOU WERE LOOKING FOR CHAMATAKA, WEREN'T YOU?

THAT RASCAL STOLE A HONEY-COMB FROM MY CAVE. WAIT TILL I GET MY HANDS ON HIM.

COME ALONG. I'LL SHOW YOU WHERE HE IS.

THERE HE IS.

GRRR!

BABLOO!

STOP!

HMMM! THAT JACKAL IS TOO FAST FOR BABLOO.

93

FORTUNE HELPS THOSE WHO HELP THEMSELVES

Script: Toni Patel
Illustrations: Ram Waeerkar

THE COURT OF RAJA KETAN ATTRACTED TALENTED YOUNG MEN FROM THE ENTIRE COUNTRY WHO HOPED TO GET EMPLOYMENT IN HIS SERVICE. MADHO PRASAD WAS ONE SUCH. LIKE THE OTHERS, HE TOO HURRIED TO DO THE KING LITTLE SERVICES...

...OR LAUGHED AS LOUDLY AS THE REST AT THE KING'S SMALLEST JOKES.

HA! HA! HA!

BUT THE KING DID NOT GIVE HIM ANY WORK.

ONE DAY, A BAKER OFFERED HIM A JOB AND MADHO PRASAD ACCEPTED IT.

SO ALL DAY HE WOULD SIT AT THE BAKER'S GRINDING CORN...

...AND IN THE EVENING HE WOULD ATTEND THE KING'S COURT AS USUAL.

WHO KNOWS? FORTUNE MAY STILL SMILE ON ME SOMEDAY!

ONE DAY, AS THE KING WAS DRIVING OUT IN HIS CHARIOT, HE HAPPENED TO PASS THE BAKERY.

CAN IT REALLY BE MADHO PRASAD?

WHAT ON EARTH IS HE WORKING THERE FOR?

THE KING'S CURIOSITY WAS AROUSED...

...AND THE MOMENT MADHO PRASAD CAME TO THE COURT THAT EVENING...

THE KING RAISED HIS EYEBROWS QUESTIONINGLY AT HIM AND CLOSING HIS RIGHT FIST...

...SLOWLY TURNED IT ROUND AND ROUND, AS IF HE WERE GRINDING WHEAT.

MADHO PRASAD WAS VERY EMBARRASSED.

IF THESE PEOPLE COME TO KNOW I'M WORKING FOR A BAKER, THEY'LL LAUGH ME OUT OF COURT.

HE TOO, DECIDED TO USE MIME TO REPLY.

MY STOMACH...

...HAS FORCED ME TO WORK WITH BOTH MY HANDS...

...TO EARN TWO ANNAS.

THE KING UNDERSTOOD HIM PERFECTLY.

AH! POOR FELLOW! I MUST DO SOMETHING TO HELP HIM!

BUT THE MIMED DIALOGUE HAD A STRANGE EFFECT ON THE COURTIERS.

WHAT WERE THE KING AND MADHO PRASAD SAYING TO EACH OTHER?

THAT'S WHAT WE MUST FIND OUT.

YES. MADHO PRASAD COULD BE A SPY.

SO FROM THE NEXT DAY ONWARDS—

O MADHO PRASAD, DO HAVE A PAAN!

NO, NO HAVE ONE OF MINE!

O MADHO PRASAD, DO LOOK AT THIS TINY PERFUME BOTTLE! IT'S JUST ARRIVED FROM LUCKNOW. DO ACCEPT IT FROM ME!

BUT FINALLY, ONE OF THEM DARED ASK THE QUESTION THAT WAS UPPERMOST IN ALL THEIR MINDS.

O MADHO PRASAD, COME, COME, NOW, DO TELL US, HA! HA! I MEAN, WHAT WERE YOU SAYING IN ONE OF THOSE SECRET SIGN CONVERSATIONS YOU WERE HAVING WITH THE KING!

ALL THESE RASCALS HAVE BEEN ROBBING THE KING IN ONE WAY OR THE OTHER...

...AND NOW THEY'RE AFRAID I MIGHT HAVE FOUND THEM OUT.

THIS IS MY CHANCE TO MAKE SOME MONEY.

WELL YOU SEE, BY CLOSING HIS RIGHT HAND, THE KING WARNED ME NOT TO DISCLOSE ROYAL SECRETS TO ANY ONE...

...AND BY THE CIRCULAR MOVEMENT OF HIS HAND, HE WAS ENQUIRING IF I HAD TOURED THE TOWN ON INSPECTION, AS HE HAD ORDERED.

OF COURSE, I BY MY GESTURES, IN RETURN ASSURED THE KING THAT HIS SECRETS WERE SAFE WITH ME...

...THAT NOT ONE OF THESE SECRETS WOULD ESCAPE FROM ME...

...AND THAT IN TWO DAYS TIME I WOULD HAVE PROOF OF ALL I HAD DISCOVERED, TO PLACE BEFORE THE KING.

WHAT ARE WE TO DO? WE ARE LOST IF THE KING LEARNS OF OUR ACTIVITIES.

WHAT SHALL WE DO? WELL, WE CAN SILENCE HIM FOREVER. TIE A STONE ROUND HIS NECK AND DROWN HIM IN THE RIVER.

YES! YES! GET RID OF THE RASCAL!

BUT WHEN HE DISAPPEARS THE KING WILL KNOW AT ONCE WE DID IT!

AND WE'LL BE IN GREATER TROUBLE THAN EVER!

OF COURSE! WHY DIDN'T WE THINK OF IT BEFORE? GIVE HIM A LARGE SUM OF MONEY TO KEEP HIM QUIET!

EACH ONE CONTRIBUTED GENEROUSLY—

AND A HEAVY PURSE FILLED WITH GOLD COINS WAS PRESENTED TO MADHO PPASAD.

ACCEPT THIS, MADHO PRASAD AS A TOKEN OF OUR RESPECT!

MADHO PRASAD, NOW A RICH MAN, GOT HIMSELF A BEAUTIFUL HOUSE AND WENT EVERY-WHERE IN AN OPEN PALANQUIN.

PRETTY SOON, THE KING WHO WAS OUT ON ONE OF HIS INSPECTIONS, CAME ACROSS MADHO PPASAD ON HIS PALANQUIN.

WHO HAVE WE HERE? IT'S MADHO PRASAD!

WHAT A STRANGE MAN YOU ARE. ONE DAY I SEE YOU GRINDING CORN FOR A LIVE-LIHOOD. THE NEXT, I SEE YOU BORNE ABOUT ON A PALANQUIN. HOW DID YOU MANAGE TO BECOME RICH SO SUDDENLY?

YOUR HIGHNESS, IT WAS ALL YOUR DOING. I OWE ALL MY PRESENT PROSPERITY TO YOU.

WHEN HE HAD RELATED THE STORY IN EVERY DETAIL, THE KING SHOOK WITH LAUGHTER.

HO! HO! HO! YOU ARE A CLEVER MAN, MADHO PRASAD AND QUICK-WITTED TOO!

YOU SHALL BE MY MINISTER OF STATE. THEN MY COURTIERS WILL REALLY HAVE SOMETHING TO WORRY ABOUT!

THE REMEDY FOR BALDNESS

Story by Lalita Kodikal

Illustrations: V.B. Halbe

100

WHY SHOULD I THINK OF A MANGO?

THERE'S NO REASON WHY YOU SHOULD.

BUT IF YOU THINK OF A MANGO, THEN THE MEDICINE WILL HAVE NO EFFECT.

SO DON'T THINK OF A MANGO.

I WON'T! I WON'T!

EARLY THE FOLLOWING MORNING—

WELL, I'VE HAD MY BATH.

NOW I'LL RUB IN THE OIL.

I'M SURE THIS WILL WORK. ONLY...

...I MUST NOT... MUST NOT...

102

103

CLEVER STEFAN

A Serbian Folktale

Illustrations : V.B. Halbe

Based on a story sent by
D. Antony Rajesh
2/8, Radha Niwas,
Maharashtra Nagar,
Bhandup Bombay 400 078.

Readers' Choice

MANY YEARS AGO SERBIA* WAS CONQUERED BY TURKEY.

THE LAND WAS RULED BY THE TURKISH PASHAS WHO LORDED IT OVER THE LOCAL PEASANTS. ONE SUCH WAS JEMAL PASHA —

THERE GOES JEMAL PASHA! HE'S A FAIR MAN, BUT HE IS VERY STRICT.

YES, BUT I WISH HE WOULDN'T IMPOSE SUCH HEAVY TAXES ON US.

AND I WISH HE'D STOP CONFISCATING OUR PROPERTY IF WE DON'T PAY THE TAXES ON TIME.

NOW JEMAL PASHA WAS ON A TAX-COLLECTING MISSION.

STEFAN! YOU HAVE NOT PAID YOUR TAXES. PAY UP AT ONCE, OR ELSE...

BUT, MY LORD, I DON'T HAVE THE MONEY...

I DON'T WANT TO LISTEN TO EXCUSES. I'LL JUST HAVE TO CONFISCATE YOUR HORSE.

OH, NO! PLEASE DON'T DO THAT! HE'S MY PET AND I CAN'T DO WITHOUT HIM.

* MODERN YUGOSLAVIA

104

STEFAN, I HAVE A DUTY TO PERFORM, THE HORSE NOW BELONGS TO THE TURKISH GOVERNMENT. SO STAND ASIDE.

AND JEMAL PASHA RODE AWAY LEADING STEFAN'S HORSE.

JEMAL MAY BE DUTY-BOUND... BUT THE TURKS HAVE NO RIGHT TO RULE OUR LAND AND TAKE OUR PROPERTY. BUT HOW CAN I GET BACK MY HORSE?

NOW JEMAL PASHA HAD A VERY FOOLISH WIFE. ONE DAY STEFAN CAME UPON HER SITTING ON A ROCK.

THERE'S JEMAL PASHA'S WIFE WATERING MY HORSE. I'LL HAVE A WORD WITH HER.

GOOD MORNING.

GOOD MORNING. AND WHERE DO YOU COME FROM?

FROM THE OTHER WORLD!

REALLY! AND HOW IS MY POOR SON, MUSTAFA, FARING THERE?

105

HEE HEE HEE! SHE'S SWALLOWED THE BAIT!

HE'S ALL RIGHT. BUT HE DOESN'T HAVE MUCH MONEY, POOR FELLOW.

OH, MY POOR SON. AND HE'S SO FOND OF TOBACCO AND BLACK COFFEE.

DO ME A FAVOUR. GIVE THIS PURSE TO HIM. IT'S FULL OF GOLD COINS.

MOST CERTAINLY. HEE HEE!

I'LL SEE THAT YOUR SON GETS THIS.

WHO WAS THAT FELLOW?

HE'S FROM THE OTHER WORLD. AND I GAVE HIM A BAG OF GOLD COINS FOR OUR SON.

WHAT! THE SCOUNDREL! HE'S TRICKED YOU. HERE, HOLD THE HORSE.

107

STOP!

HEE HEE HEE! THAT'S FOOLED HIM.

HELP! KEEP OFF!

STOP! YOU RASCAL!

WHERE'S THE BAG OF GOLD COINS?

WHAT GOLD COINS, MY LORD?

DON'T STALL ME!

MY LORD, I DON'T HAVE ANY GOLD COINS WITH ME. I'M BUT A POOR MILLER.

JEMAL PASHA SWIFTLY SEARCHED THE BAFFLED MILLER.

BUT HE COULD NOT FIND THE GOLD COINS. AT LAST IT DAWNED ON JEMAL PASHA THAT HE HAD BEEN TRICKED. HE RACED BACK.

PUFF! PUFF!

108

WIFE! HERE I AM... WHY, WHERE'S THE HORSE?

THAT NICE YOUNG MAN CAME BACK HERE AND RETURNED THE GOLD COINS.

OH! THAT'S GOOD. BUT WHY WOULD HE DO THAT?

YOU SEE, ACCORDING TO HIM, OUR SON HAS WON A LOTTERY AND HE HAS PLENTY OF MONEY. BUT HE WANTS A HORSE BADLY.

SO I GAVE HIM THE HORSE TO GIVE TO OUR SON.

OH, NO!

HE'S NOWHERE TO BE SEEN. THE SCOUNDREL HE'S TRICKED US THOROUGHLY.

STEFAN RODE MERRILY AWAY TO A NEIGHBOURING COUNTRY, HAPPY AT HAVING GOT HIS HORSE BACK.

THE ADVENTURES OF SUPPANDI – 8

Readers' Choice

Illustrations Ram Waeerkar

Based on a story sent by Sandesh Parrikar Goa

ONE MORNING —

I NEED A MATCHBOX, SUPPANDI.

I'LL GO AND BUY ONE, SIR.

ON THE WAY BACK FROM THE SHOP —

I HOPE THIS MATCHBOX IS FRESH...

...I'LL TRY A MATCHSTICK TO MAKE SURE...

...AAH! LIGHTS WELL!

THIS ONE TOO, IS ALL RIGHT.

LATER, AT HOME —

THE MATCHBOX, SUPPANDI.

HERE YOU ARE, SIR. IT'S A VERY FRESH ONE, TOO!

I TRIED ALL THE MATCHSTICKS ON THE WAY HOME!

??

Kalia
THE CROW

Illustrations:
RAM WAEERKAR

I WONDER WHAT'S GOING ON THERE.

RABBITS FIGHTING.

IT'S DOOB DOOB AND CHAMATAKA!

RUN!

THEY WERE PLAYING... BUT WHAT A CROWD HAD COLLECTED AROUND THEM.

WHY DON'T WE HAVE A FIGHT TOO.

A FIGHT?

BUT WHY SHOULD WE FIGHT?

A SHAM FIGHT, YOU DOPE!

I'LL HIT YOU AND THEN YOU HIT ME... NOT TOO HARD OF COURSE.

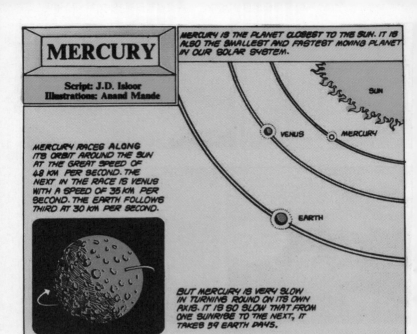

MERCURY

Script: J.D. Isloor
Illustrations: Anand Mande

MERCURY IS THE PLANET CLOSEST TO THE SUN. IT IS ALSO THE SMALLEST AND FASTEST MOVING PLANET IN OUR SOLAR SYSTEM.

SUN

VENUS

MERCURY

EARTH

MERCURY RACES ALONG ITS ORBIT AROUND THE SUN AT THE GREAT SPEED OF 48 KM PER SECOND. THE NEXT IN THE RACE IS VENUS WITH A SPEED OF 35 KM PER SECOND. THE EARTH FOLLOWS THIRD AT 30 KM PER SECOND.

BUT MERCURY IS VERY SLOW IN TURNING ROUND ON ITS OWN AXIS. IT IS SO SLOW THAT FROM ONE SUNRISE TO THE NEXT, IT TAKES 59 EARTH DAYS.

THE ANCIENT GREEKS WHO DISCOVERED MERCURY IN 3000 B.C. KNEW THAT IT MOVED VERY FAST. THAT'S WHY THEY NAMED IT HERMES, AFTER THE SWIFT MESSENGER OF THE GODS. MERCURY IS ITS ROMAN NAME. INDIANS CALL IT BUDHA AND ASSOCIATE IT WITH INTELLIGENCE.

MERCURY IS ABOUT THE SIZE OF PLUTO, THE PLANET FARTHEST FROM THE SUN AND IS SLIGHTLY LARGER THAN OUR MOON. ITS DIAMETER IS ONLY 4880 KM. IT WOULD JUST FIT INTO THE ATLANTIC OCEAN WERE IT TO BE BROUGHT ON TO THE EARTH.

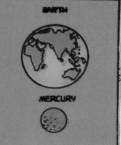

BEING CLOSEST TO THE SUN, MERCURY RECEIVES MAXIMUM HEAT AND LIGHT. THE SUN LOOKS 3 TIMES BIGGER ON MERCURY THAN IT DOES TO US ON EARTH AND SHINES FIERCELY BECAUSE MERCURY HAS NO ATMOSPHERE. ITS DAY-TIME TEMPERATURE IS AS HIGH AS 400°C. AT NIGHT THE TEMPERATURE DROPS TO −200°C

IT IS NOT EASY TO SEE MERCURY FROM THE EARTH BECAUSE OF ITS CLOSENESS TO THE SUN. THE SUN'S BRIGHTNESS DOES NOT ALLOW US TO SEE DETAILS OF ITS SURFACE.

BUT THE PLANET HAS BEEN PHOTOGRAPHED BY THE MARINER-10 SPACECRAFT WHEN IT FLEW CLOSE TO MERCURY IN 1975. THE PHOTOGRAPHS SHOW ITS SURFACE TO BE JUST LIKE OUR MOON – FULL OF CRATERS, HIGHLANDS AND PLAINS.

DID YOU KNOW?

Script: Swarn Khandpur
Illustrations: Ashok Dongre

The word Rupee has evolved from the Sanskrit term *Raupya* which means wrought silver.

Although the date of origin of coinage in India is not certain, coins as currency began to be widely used during the Mauryan and Gupta periods. But it was Sher Shah Sur who issued coins in silver by the name of *Rupiya* and made them standard currency throughout his empire. He also issued copper *Paisas*.

Throughout the Mughal period, the Rupiya remained the standard unit of currency.

Among the Indo - Europeans, the Portuguese, who were the first to establish a mint in Goa, adopted the word *Rupia* for their coins in 1775.

When the English introduced their own coins they changed the word *Rupiya* to *Rupee*. They issued one rupee, half-rupee and quarter-rupee coins in silver.

With the advent of freedom, the rupee continued to be divided along the old pattern of quarters. But with the introduction of the decimal system on April 1, 1957 the rupee became equivalent to 100 paise.

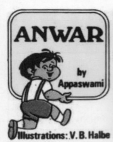

How to whiten charcoal

Illustrations: Ram Waeerkar

Adapted from the folktale as told by the late Saguna Manjeshwar.

ONE DAY BHONDURAM FOUND A PIECE OF CHARCOAL ON THE STREET.

POOR THING! IT'S SO BLACK!

DON'T BE SAD, LITTLE ONE.

I'LL MAKE YOU WHITE.

UNCLE!

YES?

IT'S BHONDU THE SIMPLETON.

HOW CAN I MAKE THIS CHARCOAL WHITE?

WHY! THAT'S EASY...

...WASH IT WITH MILK.

MILK, EH?

BHONDU WENT TO THE MILKMAN.

UNCLE...ER...PLEASE GIVE ME SOME MILK.

120

...AND BEGAN TO WASH THE PIECE OF COAL WITH SOAP AND WATER.

HEY, BHONDU. COME TO PLAY!

I CAN'T! I HAVE BETTER THINGS TO DO.

WHAT ARE YOU DOING?

HOW DUMB CAN YOU GET! I AM WASHING THIS CHARCOAL SO THAT IT BECOMES WHITE.

HAH! FOR THAT YOU MUST RUB IT ON A GRINDING STONE. DON'T YOU KNOW THAT, CLEVER ONE?

OH!

OF COURSE I KNOW THAT... NOW LEAVE ME ALONE.

SO BHONDU BEGAN TO RUB THE PIECE OF CHARCOAL ON A GRINDING STONE.

SOMETIME LATER—

WHAT ARE YOU DOING, SON?

I...ER...

121

MAKE YOUR OWN LETTER HOLDER

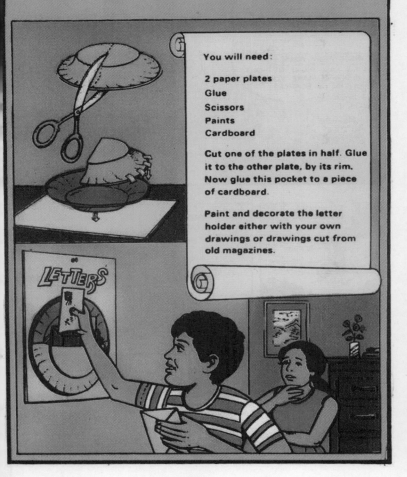

You will need:

2 paper plates
Glue
Scissors
Paints
Cardboard

Cut one of the plates in half. Glue it to the other plate, by its rim. Now glue this pocket to a piece of cardboard.

Paint and decorate the letter holder either with your own drawings or drawings cut from old magazines.

SURESH'S CAT
Illustrations: Ashok Dongre

Based on a story sent
by Sanjay Colaso.
Margao, Goa

SURESH'S CAT WAS GETTING ON HIS NERVES.

YOU ARE SO DISOBEDIENT AND NAUGHTY!! I'LL HAVE TO DO SOMETHING ABOUT YOU!

COME ON NOW — JUMP IN — WE'RE GOING FOR A LITTLE WALK!

FAR AWAY FROM HOME —

ALL RIGHT, GET OUT AND MAKE YOURSELF SCARCE!

MEEEOW!

NOW TO GET BACK TO A PEACEFUL HOUSE!

BUT—

OH! WHICH TURNING DO I TAKE?

I'M LOST… HEY! THERE'S THE CAT!

IT MUST BE GOING HOME… I'LL FOLLOW IT.

AND SOON SURESH STOOD IN FRONT OF HIS OWN HOUSE.

YOU CRAZY CAT! YOU BROUGHT ME HOME!

PURR… PURR…

OKAY, OKAY! WE'LL HAVE TO TRY TO GET ALONG WITH EACH OTHER FROM NOW ON!

TWO FROGS

Illustrations Ashok Dongre

Readers' Choice

Based on a story sent by Mirza Gasanfar Ali Baig, Hyderabad

TWO FROGS WENT TO A DAIRY.

WHEN THEY WERE INSIDE—

I WONDER WHAT ALL THESE BARRELS CONTAIN?

LET'S JUMP INTO ONE AND SEE WHAT'S IN IT.

AND SO—

SPLASH

WHAT'S THIS?

IT'S MILK.

OH DEAR, OH DEAR!

THERE'S NOTHING TO WORRY ABOUT. JUST KEEP SWIMMING AND YOU'LL BE ALL RIGHT.

THAT'S WHAT YOU THINK! I CAN'T STAND THIS SMELL! I'M GETTING OUT!

AGAIN AND AGAIN THE FROG TRIED TO CLIMB OUT OF THE BARREL.

BUT EACH TIME HE SLIPPED AND FELL...

SPLASH

... AND FINALLY —

GLUB GLUB GLUB glub

HE HAS DROWNED! MY POOR FRIEND!

THE OTHER FROG KEPT THRASHING ABOUT.

AFTER SOME TIME—

THIS MILK IS BECOMING THICKER AND THICKER...

... AND THICKER.

BY MORNING THE MILK HAD TURNED INTO BUTTER AND THE FROG JUMPED OUT OF THE BARREL, VERY TIRED, BUT SAFE.

THE RAIN-MAKER

Illustrations: S. N. Sawant

Based on a story sent by Ramesh M.K., Bombay

ONCE THERE WAS AN ASTROLOGER. EVERYBODY IN HIS VILLAGE CAME TO HIM TO HAVE THEIR FORTUNES TOLD.

AND AS HIS FEES WERE HIGH, HE MADE A LOT OF MONEY.

ONE YEAR THERE WAS A DROUGHT.

MY FIELDS ARE PARCHED.

MINE, TOO.

WHEN WILL THE RAINS COME?

IN DESPAIR, THE HEADMAN WENT TO THE ASTROLOGER.

TELL ME, WHEN WILL IT RAIN?

SOON.

GIVE US A DEFINITE DATE.

WE CAN WAIT NO LONGER.

WHAT SHOULD I DO NOW?

128

129

Kalia
THE CROW

Script:
DENIS

Illustrations:
RAM WAEERKAR

WHAT'S HAPPENED, CHAMATAKA? ARE YOU ILL?

SSHH...! DON'T DISTURB HIM. HE'S FASTING.

FASTING?

I AM REPENTING FOR ALL MY PAST SINS, KALIA.

THAT'S NICE! BUT I MUST BE OFF. BYE!

PEACE BE WITH YOU!

I'D BETTER KEEP AN EYE ON THESE TWO.

GOT RID OF HIM AT LAST.

I'M HUNGRY. TIME TO EAT SOME HONEY.

WAIT! WHAT IF SOMEBODY COMES ALONG?

TELL THEM I AM INSIDE — MEDITATING.

MEDITATION, PAAH! HE HAS RUSHED BACK TO THE HONEY COMBS HE STOLE FROM BABLOO'S CAVE.

OH! OH!

JUST THEN—

I'M HUNGRY, KEECHU.

I TOO. WISH WE COULD FIND SOME CARROTS.

HEY, RUN! IT'S DOOS DOOB! CHAMATAKA IS HERE, TOO.

WAIT! DON'T RUN AWAY. CHAMATAKA WON'T HARM YOU...

RIGHT! I'VE GIVEN UP HUNTING.

DON'T YOU SEE? I HAVEN'T EVEN MOVED TO CHASE YOU LIKE BEFORE.

THAT'S TRUE.

COME— BE MY FRIENDS.

YOU WILL FIND SOME JUICY CARROTS IN THERE.

CARROTS! WE LOVE THEM.

AND WE'RE HUNGRY.

THEN GO IN. EAT AS MUCH AS YOU CAN. WE WON'T HARM YOU.

THE TWO RABBITS WALKED IN UNSUSPECTINGLY.

OH NO! THE RABBITS ARE TRAPPED.

SUDDENLY—

THUM THUMP

GR... SOMEBODY STOLE MY HONEYCOMBS. WHERE WERE YOU LAST NIGHT?

I...I... HAVE GIVEN UP STEALING. I AM NOW ON A FAST...

YOU TOO CAN COME IN, BABLOO. LOTS OF HONEY IN HERE.

SO YOU ARE FASTING, HUH!

RASCAL! WILL YOU NEVER IMPROVE?

TIME FOR ME TO LEAVE.

GO—JOIN YOUR FRIEND.

BLUB...GLUG... AH...

HE HAS SWALLOWED A LOT OF WATER!

BROTHER CHAMATAKA HAS BROKEN HIS FAST AT LAST. HA, HA, HA!

132

Make your own **MAGIC RINGS**

You will need: A strip of paper (about 4 cm x 30 cm or longer)
Scissors
Glue

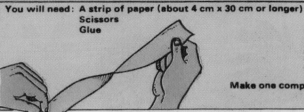

Make one complete twist.

Glue the two ends together.

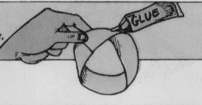

Draw a line along the centre all the way around and then cut all along the line.

The result is not two rings, as you might have supposed, but one big ring, double the size of the original ring.

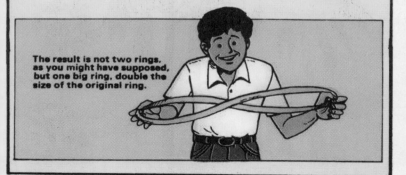

133

OUR PALMS

Script: J.D Isloor • Illustrations: J.P. Irani

IT IS EASY TO IDENTIFY A PALM TREE. IT HAS A LONG CYLINDRICAL STEM, CROWNED WITH A TUFT OF LEAVES. AND IT HAS NO BRANCHES. THERE ARE SEVERAL TYPES OF PALMS:

COCONUT PALM

PALMYRA PALM

ARECA PALM

DATE PALM

MALABAR SAGO PALM

RATTAN CANE PALM

COCONUT PALM

THIS MAJESTIC PALM IS KNOWN AS 'KALPA VRIKSHA' IN HINDU MYTHOLOGY. IT MEANS 'WISH TREE' IN SANSKRIT. THE TREE IS SYMBOLIC OF LONGEVITY. ITS FRUIT, THE COCONUT IS SACRED TO HINDUS.

PEOPLE LIVING IN COASTAL AREAS, ESPECIALLY THOSE WHO DEPEND UPON THE SEA FOR THEIR LIVELIHOOD OFFER COCONUT FRUITS TO VARUNA, THE GOD OF THE SEAS. 'COCONUT DAY' IS CONSIDERED MOST SACRED FOR THIS OFFERING.

THIS PALM CAN GROW TO A HEIGHT OF 25 M. THE TRUNK IS MARKED WITH SEMI-CIRCULAR SCARS. THEY INDICATE THE PLACES WHERE NEW BOUGHS, NOW FALLEN, HAD SPROUTED. YOU CAN TELL THE AGE OF THE TREE BY COUNTING THE SCARS TEN TO TWELVE SCARS REPRESENT ONE YEAR AS BOUGHS SPROUT AT THE RATE OF ABOUT ONE PER MONTH.

A WELL CULTIVATED TREE CAN YIELD ABOUT 300 TO 400 COCONUTS PER YEAR, BUT THE AVERAGE YIELD IN OUR COUNTRY IS MUCH LESS.

YOU WILL NOT FIND ANOTHER TREE AS USEFUL AS THE COCONUT PALM. EVERY PART OF THE TREE IS USEFUL. THE NUT, WHEN TENDER, CONTAINS DELICIOUS WATER AND SWEET FLESH. IT IS NOT ONLY THIRST-QUENCHING, BUT VERY NUTRITIOUS, TOO. IT CONTAINS SUGAR, MINERALS AND VITAMINS.

WHEN THE FRUIT IS RIPE IT IS USED IN COOKING. IT IS THE FAVOURITE INGREDIENT IN MANY FOOD PREPARATIONS OF PEOPLE LIVING IN THE COASTAL REGIONS.

THE DRIED KERNEL IS KNOWN AS 'COPRA.' THIS IS USED IN MAKING DRY CHUTNEYS AND EXTRACTING OIL. COCONUT OIL IS AN EDIBLE OIL USED NOT ONLY IN COOKING BUT ALSO IN COSMETICS, MEDICINES AND SOAP-MAKING.

AFTER THE OIL HAS BEEN EXTRACTED FROM COPRA, WHATEVER IS LEFT BEHIND ARE CALLED OIL-CAKES. THESE ARE USED AS CATTLE FEED.

THE FIBRE COVERING THE SHELL IS CALLED COIR. THE COIR IS USED IN MAKING ROPES, CARPETS, DOORMATS, MATTRESSES AND BRUSHES. THE COIR EARNS SUBSTANTIAL FOREIGN EXCHANGE FOR INDIA.

A VERY SWEET SAP CALLED 'NEERA' IS COLLECTED BY MAKING A CUT ON THE YOUNG TREE. WHEN FERMENTED, IT BECOMES 'TODDY' WHICH IS AN INTOXICATING DRINK.

BROOMS ARE MADE FROM THE LEAF-RIBS.

THE COCONUT TREE IS RIGHTLY CALLED 'GREEN GOLD.'

136

THE RIVER OF DIAMONDS

READERS' CHOICE

Illustrations: S.N. Sawant

Based on a story sent by
Ramandeep Bedi, Patiala.

SHYAM HAD DECIDED TO GO TO THE CITY. AS HE WAS ABOUT TO LEAVE—

SON, I'VE NOTHING TO GIVE YOU...

...EXCEPT THIS SMALL DIAMOND.

MOTHER...I,...

TAKE IT!

SO SHYAM TOOK THE DIAMOND, TUCKED IT INTO HIS DHOTI...

...BID HIS MOTHER A TEARFUL FAREWELL...

...AND SET OUT. AT NOON, AS HE WAS HALF-WAY THROUGH A JUNGLE—

ROBBERS!

HAND OVER YOUR BELONGINGS!

A-ALL RIGHT!

137

138

139

THE WEATHER FORECAST

Based on a story sent by Paominlal Singsit,
Keithelmanbi, Senapati Dist.,
Manipur 795122.

Illustrations : Anand Mande

ONCE TWO MEN WERE MOTORING IN A LONELY PART OF AMERICA—

WHAT A VAST, DESOLATE AREA!

YES, THERE'S NOT A SOUL TO BE SEEN.

BUT—

LOOK, THERE'S A RED INDIAN!

LET'S GO TALK TO HIM.

FORTUNATELY, THE RED INDIAN SPOKE ENGLISH—

HOW!

ER... GOOD MORNING!

YES! NICE, SUNNY MORNING ISN'T IT?

IT WON'T BE LIKE THAT IN A FEW DAYS' TIME!

WHAT DO YOU MEAN?

IT WILL RAIN HEAVILY FOR THREE DAYS AND AFTER THAT THERE WILL BE STRONG WINDS FOR TWO DAYS...

...AND THEN IT WILL BE SUNNY ONCE AGAIN.

WONDERFUL! THESE PRIMITIVE RED INDIANS KNOW MORE ABOUT THE SECRETS OF NATURE THAN WE DO.

BUT HOW DO YOU KNOW THAT?

I HEARD IT ON THE RADIO!

EH!

Meet the OWL

Script : Vaijayanti Wagle

Illustrations : Ajit Vasaikar

THE LAST RAYS OF THE EVENING SUN FADE AWAY. HIDDEN IN A ROCKY LEDGE ON THE OUTSKIRTS OF TOWN, THE OWL BLINKS OPEN HIS ENORMOUS EYES.

HE FLIES OUT AND SETTLES ON HIS FAVOURITE PERCH. BU BO, BU BO, HE ANNOUNCES SOLEMNLY.

A FAINT RUSTLING SOUND REACHES HIS EARS. HE TURNS HIS HEAD ALMOST RIGHT AROUND TO LOOK FOR THE SOURCE OF THE SOUND...

ISN'T IT WONDERFUL THAT HE CAN LOOK ALL AROUND HIM WITHOUT STIRRING FROM HIS PERCH?

...AND IS JUST IN TIME TO SEE A RAT RUSH INTO A THICKET.

PRESENTLY A FAINT NIBBLING SOUND REACHES HIS EARS. THE RAT IS GNAWING ON A BLADE OF GRASS.

GUIDED BY THE SOUND, THE OWL SWOOPS AS SILENTLY AS A WHISPER.

141

THE RAT DOES NOT REALISE WHAT IS HAPPENING UNTIL THE OWL'S POWERFUL CLAWS DIG INTO ITS BODY...

... AND THEN IT'S TOO LATE.

OWLS CAN CATCH PREY IN ABSOLUTE DARKNESS, RELYING ON THEIR SENSE OF HEARING ALONE.

OOPS! THE OWL HAS SWALLOWED THE RAT IN A SINGLE GULP!

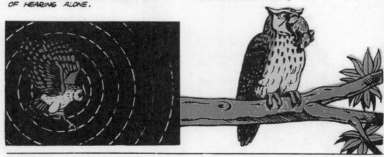

WHAT HE CANNOT DIGEST, WILL BE PRESSED INTO A HARD PELLET AND PASSED OUT THROUGH HIS MOUTH.

SOME WEEKS LATER WE SEE OUR FRIEND AGAIN. THIS TIME INSTEAD OF SWOOPING ON RATS, HE IS FLYING AROUND A FEMALE OWL.

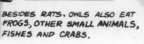

BESIDES RATS, OWLS ALSO EAT FROGS, OTHER SMALL ANIMALS, FISHES AND CRABS.

THEY'RE GOING TO RAISE A FAMILY...

...AND AS OWLS DON'T BUILD NESTS, THIS HOLLOW COULD BE JUST THE PLACE FOR THE FEMALE TO LAY HER EGGS IN.

SHE USUALLY LAYS FOUR CREAMY, OVAL EGGS. AND SHE SITS ON THE EGGS TO INCUBATE THEM.

FIVE WEEKS LATER THE FIRST EGG HAS HATCHED. THE OTHERS WILL FOLLOW SOON AFTER.

YOU HAVE JUST READ ABOUT THE GREAT HORNED OWL. THERE ARE MANY KINDS OF OWLS FOUND IN INDIA.

BARN OWL

COLLARED SCOPS OWL

BROWN FISH OWL

BARRED JUNGLE OWLET

THE SPOTTED OWL

THE CLEVER PRAWN
Illustrations : Ashok Dongre

READERS' CHOICE

ONE DAY A CAT CAUGHT A PRAWN.

DON'T EAT ME, PLEASE!

WHY NOT?

GIVE ME A CHANCE! LET'S RUN A RACE.

A RACE?

IF YOU WIN YOU CAN EAT ME, BUT IF I WIN YOU MUST LET ME GO.

AGREED!

ON YOUR MARKS... GET SET...

GO!

THE PRAWN HUNG ON TO THE CAT'S TAIL...

...AND WHEN THEY REACHED THE FINISHING LINE...

...LEAPT IN FRONT!

Y-YOU'RE ALREADY HERE!

I'VE BEEN WAITING HERE FOR AGES!

AND SO THE CLEVER PRAWN SAVED ITSELF!

144

Shikari Shambu

Script:
Luis M Fernandes
Illustrations:
V.B. Halbe

145

146

147

HAVE A HAIRCUT

This story by Dr (Mrs) Kavery Bhatt won a Consolation Prize in the Tinkle Original Story Competition.

Script: Dev Nadkarni
Illustrations: V.B. Halbe

AND SO, THE BOYS GOT TO WORK IN AN UNOCCUPIED BACK ROOM OF RAFIQ'S HOUSE.

THIS IS GOING TO BE FUN!

PHEW! THIS IS HARD WORK!

WHERE DO WE GET THE MONEY TO BUY ALL THE EQUIPMENT FROM?

LET'S MAKE DO WITH WHAT WE HAVE, MANI.

RAFIQ, YOUR SISTER RAZIA COULD HELP US, PERHAPS.

HMM... I'LL GET HER SCISSORS, COMBS AND MAYBE EVEN HER SHAMPOOS AND PERFUMES. I'LL BE BACK.

AND I'LL GET A LEMON.. CURES DANDRUFF YOU KNOW— AND EGGS FOR LONGER HAIR.

GREAT! AND DON'T FORGET A MIRROR!

A FEW HOURS LATER—

THERE! WE'RE ALMOST READY.

LET'S PUT UP THE BILL-BOARD.

NOW WE'RE IN BUSINESS!

UNIQUE HAIR DRESSING SALOON
ORDINARY RS 0·50
SPECIAL RS·1·00
SUPER
SPEC 2·00

NOT YET! WE MUST GET SOMEONE TO INAUGURATE IT FIRST.

WHO SHALL WE CALL?

HEY, THERE GOES MANI'S GRANDFATHER ON HIS EVENING WALK.

GOOD EVENING, GRANDPA. WE CORDIALLY INVITE YOU AS CHIEF GUEST TO INAUGURATE...

ME? AS CHIEF GUEST... TO INAUGURATE WHAT?

WE'RE STARTING A SALOON, GRANDPA— TO SERVE THE PEOPLE OF OUR COLONY...

AND WE DO BELIEVE IN DIGNITY OF LABOUR...

OKAY, OKAY, BOYS, I'LL BE HAPPY TO INAUGURATE YOUR SALOON!

DEAR, DEAR, GRANDPA.

HOW NICE!

150

AT THE SALOON—

GOD BLESS YOU CHILDREN, GOD BLESS YOU!

THANK YOU VERY MUCH, GRANDPA.

MY PLEASURE, BOYS...AND DO YOUR JOB WELL.

WE SHOULD START BY GIVING A FREE HAIRCUT TO A DESERVING PERSON.

I'LL GO GET SOMEBODY.

A LITTLE WHILE LATER—

WAA...WAA... BUT I DON'T WANT A HAIRCUT!

O, YOU DO— LOOK AT ALL THE JUNGLE!

IT WAS CHANDU, MANI'S 6-YEAR-OLD BROTHER.

NOW YOU JUST SIT HERE.

THERE YOU ARE, JAI, YOU CAN BEGIN.

151

SNIP... SNIP...

SNIP... SNIP...

GET UP NOW, CHANDU. GO HOME. AMMA WILL BE HAPPY WITH YOUR TRIMMED HAIR. AND DON'T CRY. HERE, HAVE THIS TOFFEE.

GET SOMEONE ELSE RAFIQ! WE CAN'T SIT IDLE.

YES. YES, I WILL.

HI, UNCLE MALLICK, WOULD YOU LIKE A HAIR-CUT?

ME? A HAIR-CUT?

S...SORRY UNCLE...

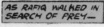

AS RAFIQ WALKED IN SEARCH OF PREY—

O GOD! THAT'S RAZIA!

MY PERFUME, MY SHAMPOO— EVERYTHING'S MISSING...

JUST THEN—

HELLO SON! HIDING FROM SOMEONE?

Y-YES. -ER-NO. O, HELLO, UNCLE RAJAN!

WHAT'S THE MATTER, MY BOY. HERE, HAVE A TOFFEE.

THANKS, UNCLE.

CAN I HELP YOU, SON?

YES, UNCLE— I MEAN— NO I... WE CAN HELP YOU.

153

154

SNIP...

SNIP...

SNIP...

THANK GOD, MY EARS ARE AT LEAST IN PLACE!

SUDDENLY— SO THIS IS WHERE MY HAIR-DO KIT HAS LANDED...I SHOULD'VE KNOWN...

AND LOOK WHAT THEY'VE DONE TO MY CHANDU! OH! AND ISN'T THAT OUR MIRROR?

YOU WICKED BEASTS!

TAKE THAT... AND THAT!

SO AFTER ONLY ONE DAY THE 'UNIQUE HAIR-DRESSING SALOON' WAS FORCED TO CLOSE DOWN.

AS FOR POOR COL. RAJAN— HE HAD TO WEAR A CAP FOR TWO MONTHS! BUT HE STILL REMAINED A GOOD FRIEND OF THE BOYS.

HELLO KIDS, WHAT'S UP THIS TIME?

THE FOLLY OF IMITATION

Readers' Choice

Illustrations: Ram Waeerkar

Based on a story sent by Shashin S. Kowshik, Bombay.

EARLY ONE MORNING IN A VILLAGE —

?

ER... SIR, I SAW YOU GOING ROUND YOUR HOUSE SEVERAL TIMES. WHY DID YOU DO THAT?

SO THAT I'LL HAVE A GOOD HARVEST AND BECOME RICH.

SO THAT'S THE WAY TO BECOME RICH!

THE MAN WAS A ROBBER AND SO THE FOLLOWING DAY —

I'LL GO AROUND THIS HOUSE A FEW TIMES BEFORE BREAKING IN.

WHY IS THAT MAN WALKING AROUND MY HOUSE? HE MUST BE A THIEF!

THE HOUSE-HOLDER CALLED HIS SERVANTS,

DRIVE THAT MAN AWAY!

!

NOTHING OF THIS SORT HAPPENED TO THE FARMER!

BUT ONE THING IS CERTAIN I COULD NEVER BECOME RICH THIS WAY!

AND THE ROBBER RAN FOR HIS LIFE.

157

A MAN WAS CROSSING A FOREST—

SUDDENLY—

EH...

DON'T MOVE!

QUICK, HAND OVER EVERYTHING YOU HAVE.

I...I... DON'T HAVE...

THE MAN QUICKLY SLIPPED A ROLL OF NOTES INTO THE THIEF'S POCKET.

OOOOH!

HE'S FAINTED.

158

THE THIEF WENT THROUGH ARJUN'S POCKETS.

NOTHING! WHAT A WASTE OF TIME!

H-HAS IT GONE?

WHO?

I... I SAW A SNAKE. I WAS SO SCARED!

WHERE WAS IT?

THERE IT IS!

YIEEEEEE!

I CAN'T SEE ANY SNAKE!

JUST GO AWAY, BEFORE I LOSE MY TEMPER."

THE TRAVELLER HURRIED AWAY THRILLED AT HAVING OUTWITTED THE THIEF

159

Make your own
SOAP BUBBLES

You will need:
Water, sugar, soap scrapings, a slim hollow plastic tube or a wire frame and a small piece of fine cloth.

Put four teaspoons of sugar into a glass.

Fill the glass with water and stir well until sugar dissolves.

Add one teaspoon of soap scrapings and stir until dissolved.

Strain the liquid into a cup through the piece of cloth.

Make a lollipop shape wire frame with old fuse or other wire.

Using the wire frame or slim plastic tube, you can blow enough bubbles to fill a room!

ON A COLD, WINTRY NIGHT—

BLAH! BLAH!

BIFF! PUNCH!

TAKE THAT!

LOOKS LIKE SOMEONE IS QUARRELLING.

LET OTHERS QUARREL— WHY SHOULD YOU GO OUT ?

WHAT WERE THEY QUARRELLING ABOUT?

THEY WERE QUARRELLING ABOUT WHO SHOULD TAKE MY BLANKET WHEN I CAME OUT TO WATCH THEM FIGHTING.

THE WISE FOOLS OF MOIRA

A folk tale from Goa

Script :
Luis M. Fernandes

Illustrations :
Ram Waeerkar

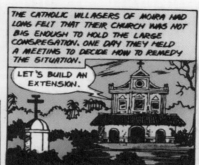

THE CATHOLIC VILLAGERS OF MOIRA HAD LONG FELT THAT THEIR CHURCH WAS NOT BIG ENOUGH TO HOLD THE LARGE CONGREGATION. ONE DAY THEY HELD A MEETING TO DECIDE HOW TO REMEDY THE SITUATION.

LET'S BUILD AN EXTENSION.

AN EXTENSION WOULD LOOK VERY UGLY.

LET'S BREAK DOWN THE WHOLE STRUCTURE AND BUILD A NEW CHURCH.

IT WOULD REQUIRE A LOT OF MONEY TO BREAK DOWN THE CHURCH AND BUILD A NEW ONE.

WHY BREAK IT DOWN AT ALL?

WHEN A COCONUT OR MANGO TREE IS STUNTED, WHAT DO WE DO?

WE LOOSEN THE SOIL AT THE BASE, DIG IT UP...

...AND LAY MANURE.

EXACTLY.

164

MANURE CAN MAKE ANYTHING GROW!

AND SO THE VILLAGERS CONVINCED THEMSELVES THAT THE CHURCH HAD GROWN BIGGER.

BUT SOME MONTHS LATER...

THERE'S TOO MUCH SPACE IN FRONT OF THE CHURCH AND TOO LITTLE BEHIND IT.

YES, THERE'S NO BALANCE.

THERE SHOULD BE EQUAL SPACE IN FRONT OF AND BEHIND THE CHURCH.

OUR ANCESTORS WHO BUILT THE CHURCH WERE NOT A VERY BRIGHT LOT, I'M AFRAID.

IT'S NO USE BLAMING OUR ANCESTORS! WE MUST BRING THE CHURCH FORWARD SOMEHOW!

HOW DO WE DO THAT?

IT'S SIMPLE.

IT WAS THE SACRISTAN OF THE CHURCH WHO HAD SPOKEN.

HE WAS NOT FROM MOIRA BUT FROM THE NEIGHBOURING VILLAGE OF ALDONA.

WHAT WOULD YOU DO IF YOU WANTED TO BRING A BIG ROCK FORWARD?

I WOULD GO BEHIND THE ROCK AND PUSH IT.

EXACTLY!

165

SO IF WE WANT TO BRING THE CHURCH FORWARD...

...WE SHOULD GO BEHIND THE CHURCH AND PUSH IT!

WHAT A SIMPLE SOLUTION!

ISN'T IT?

LET'S DO IT AT ONCE!

YES.

I'LL CALL ALL THE MEN TOGETHER.

YES, DO THAT.

SOON ALL THE ABLE-BODIED MEN OF THE VILLAGE HAD ASSEMBLED BEHIND THE CHURCH.

SHALL WE START PUSHING?

NOT YET.

IT WOULD BE EASIER TO PUSH THE CHURCH IF SOMETHING SMOOTH WAS PLACED UNDER IT.

LET'S SPREAD WOOLLEN BLANKETS IN FRONT OF THE CHURCH RIGHT UP TO THE SPOT WHERE WE WANT IT TO BE PUSHED.

AN EXCELLENT IDEA.

THE VILLAGERS GATHERED A LARGE PILE OF WOOLLEN BLANKETS AND SPREAD THEM IN FRONT OF THE CHURCH.

THERE, THAT'S DONE! NOW SHALL WE GO BEHIND AND PUSH?

YES.

I'LL STAND IN FRONT HERE AND TELL YOU WHEN TO STOP...

OTHERWISE YOU MAY PUSH IT BEYOND THE LIMIT... OR EVEN OUT OF THE COMPOUND.

YES, THAT COULD HAPPEN.

THE VILLAGERS WENT TO THE REAR...

...AND STARTED PUSHING.

HARDER! HARDER!

IN THE FRONT, THE WILY SACRISTAN QUICKLY GATHERED UP THE WOOLLEN BLANKETS...

...RAN TO HIS ROOM...

...AND KEPT THEM THERE.

THEN HE RAN OUT AGAIN, AND AFTER SOME TIME —

STOP! STOP!

IT'S REACHED THE LIMIT!

THE VILLAGERS RAN TO THE FRONT OF THE CHURCH.

SEE, ALL THE BLANKETS HAVE GONE UNDER.

THEY HAVE INDEED!

WE'VE DONE IT! WE'VE PUSHED THE CHURCH FORWARD!

THERE WAS GREAT REJOICING IN THE VILLAGE THAT DAY AND THE SACRISTAN WAS PRAISED TO THE SKIES.

Write a Letter with Your Own Invisible Ink

You will need: a lime; an old fountain pen; a cup; a sheet of white paper; a source of heat (a candle).

Squeeze the lime and collect its juice in the cup

Dip the old pen into the juice and write out a 'secret' letter on the piece of paper. After you have written 4-5 words, dip the pen again into the juice. You cannot read what you have written. Your letter is an invisible one.

To be able to read it, hold the letter close to a candle for a minute or so. The words will appear slowly in a brownish colour.

(N.B. Do not hold this letter too close to the candle, for it may catch fire.)

THE STUPID THIEF

Illustrations: Ram Waeerker

Based on a story sent by
Snigdhá Bose, Cuttack

BUDDHURAM WAS PASSING THROUGH A FOREST ONE DAY WHEN—

ROBBERS!

SO MUCH LOOT!

HE QUIETLY SLIPPED AWAY.

HUH! THIS IS LIFE! WHY TOIL AND SWEAT? I'LL ALSO BECOME A THIEF!

SO THE NEXT NIGHT, ARMED WITH A KNIFE AND A SACK, BUDDHURAM SET OUT.

THERE MUST BE PLENTY OF MONEY IN THAT HOUSE.

HE WENT ROUND THE HOUSE.

AHA! I'M IN LUCK! THIS IS OPEN!

THUD!

WHO IS THAT?

171

SOON —

WHAT A FOOL!

WHAT A FOOL!

I'LL BRING THE PRABAD NOW, MY LORD! PLEASE WAIT!

AHA!

BUDDHURAM WAITED AND WAITED.

WHY IS HE TAKING SO LONG? ...HE MUST BE BRINGING A LOT OF PRASAD.

THERE! THERE HE IS!

THIEF! RASCAL!

TAKE THIS PRASAD!

AND THIS!

AFTER A WHILE —

ENOUGH! LET HIM GO! HE'LL NEVER DO IT AGAIN!

WELL, I SUPPOSE THAT IN THIS BUSINESS TOO, YOU HAVE TO SWEAT IT OUT SOMETIMES!

JACKALS CAME TO DINNER

Illustrations: Ashok Dongre

READERS' CHOICE

Based on a story sent by Rajesh Kumar Prasad, Assam

AN OLD WOMAN WAS TAKING FOOD FOR HER SON WHO WORKED IN THE FIELDS.

SUDDENLY—

JACKALS!

WHAT HAVE YOU GOT THERE, GRANDMA?

B-SOME KHICHARI FOR MY SON.

PUT IT DOWN! NOW COME AND PRESS OUR LEGS.

?

WHILE SHE PRESSED THE LEGS OF ONE JACKAL, THE OTHERS ATE UP ALL THE KHICHARI.

?

THE OLD WOMAN RETURNED HOME SADLY—

MY POOR BOY MUST BE VERY HUNGRY.

173

THAT EVENING WHEN HER SON RETURNED—

WHAT HAPPENED? WHY DIDN'T YOU BRING MY LUNCH TODAY?

I...I HAD A STRANGE EXPERIENCE...

AND SHE TOLD HER SON WHAT HAD HAPPENED.

...I COULDN'T GET FOOD THROUGH TO YOU BECAUSE OF THE JACKALS.

THE JACKALS CONTINUED TO HARASS THE OLD WOMAN, UNTIL ONE EVENING—

LISTEN, MOTHER, I HAVE A PLAN...

SO THE NEXT DAY THE OLD WOMAN WENT TO THE FOREST AND BEGAN TO PICK FLOWERS.

WHY IS THERE NO KHICHARI TODAY?

MY SON IS DEAD. SO FOR WHOM SHOULD I BRING THE KHICHARI?

BUT I WOULD LIKE TO COOK FOR SOMEONE. WHY DON'T YOU ALL COME AND HAVE DINNER WITH ME TOMORROW?

THE NEXT EVENING THE JACKALS WENT TO THE OLD WOMAN'S HOUSE.

SHE WENT INTO THE KITCHEN AND STARTED SPRINKLING WATER ON A HOT GRIDDLE.

SIZZLE

SHE MUST BE MAKING PURIS.

OR KACHORIS!

IS THE FOOD READY?

YES. BUT I DON'T WANT YOU ALL TO FIGHT FOR THE FOOD AS YOU USUALLY DO...

...SO I WILL TIE YOU UP, FIRST.

DO IT QUICKLY THEN! WE'RE STARVING.

THE OLD WOMAN TIED UP THE JACKALS...

...AND THEN —

SON! SON! COME WITH THE IRON ROD!

SON?

175